A PROGRAMMED TEXT

USE OF THE OSCILLOSCOPE

Charles H. Roth, Jr.

Department of Electrical Engineering
The University of Texas at Austin

PRENTICE-HALL, INC., ENGLEWOOD CLIFFS, N.J.

PRENTICE-HALL INTERNATIONAL, INC., London
PRENTICE-HALL OF AUSTRALIA, PTY. LTD., Sydney
PRENTICE-HALL OF CANADA, LTD., Toronto
PRENTICE-HALL OF INDIA PRIVATE LTD., New Delhi
PRENTICE-HALL OF JAPAN, INC., Tokyo

PREFACE

This programmed text has been designed for use in a basic electrical engineering laboratory course. Since the oscilloscope is one of the most important and versatile measuring instruments, instruction in use of the oscilloscope is usually given near the beginning of such a course. The modern triggered sweep oscilloscope is a rather complex instrument with many controls and input terminals. The instruction manuals supplied with most scopes are intended for reference and are usually not suitable for teaching an inexperienced student how to operate a scope. This programmed text breaks down the process of operating a scope into a series of logical steps starting with deflection of the electron beam and continuing through proper use of the triggering controls to measure the phase difference between two waveforms. Understanding the operation of the scope is stressed at each step rather than mere manipulation of controls. Although teaching use of the scope is the primary purpose of this text, the student will also learn some general principles of electrical measurements which are applicable to other laboratory instruments.

Programmed Instruction

Programmed instruction is especially well suited to teaching the effective use of laboratory equipment. The material to be learned is broken down into a carefully designed sequence of steps or frames. Each frame explains a basic idea or presents a problem to be solved. The student then must take some positive action, which usually includes writing an answer. He thus participates actively in the learning process and "learns by doing." The correct answer is provided on the next page so that the student can immediately verify his own answer. This provides a reinforcement if the answer is correct, or correction and explanation if it is wrong. Each student can thus proceed at his own pace, going on to a new set of material only after he has mastered the previous set.

By careful study of student responses and examination results, this program has been revised and improved to remove "stumbling blocks" to student progress. The size of the steps in the program has been adjusted so that the average student will get more than 90 per cent of the answers correct as he progresses through the program. This does not imply that the program is trivial; the student is expected to reason out many things for himself. For example, he must draw his own circuit diagrams rather than being told how to hook up the circuit. Our experience with this programmed text indicates that every student who has the necessary prerequisites and who completes the program according to instructions will be able to demonstrate mastery of the material by passing a practical examination on use of the scope.

Prerequisites

This program assumes a knowledge of basic DC and AC circuits. Familiarity with circuit terms and the ability to solve simple circuits is required. No specific previous laboratory experience is assumed, but the laboratory parts of the program require the ability to hook up simple circuits and read meters.

Required Equipment

This text is intended for use with a triggered sweep oscilloscope such as the Tektronix 503 or the Tektronix 561, 561A or 561B equipped with a 2A63 differential amplifier plug-in and a 2B67 time base plug-in. The theory parts of the text are general enough to be used with almost any triggered sweep oscilloscope, but the laboratory parts will require some modification to adapt them to different scopes. When scopes other than the Tektronix 503 or 561 series are used, the laboratory instructor should prepare a list of any changes which are required for the particular scope being used. Suggestions for adapting the program to other types of scopes are given in the Teachers' Manual. Other required equipment includes oscillators, function generators, and DC power supplies which are readily available in most laboratories. Since detailed instructions for using this auxiliary equipment are not included in the program, the lab instructor should demonstrate the use of this equipment as required.

Acknowledgements

Preparation of the earlier versions of this text was supported in part by the American Society for Engineering Education Programmed Learning Project which was sponsored principally by the Ford Foundation and directed by Norman Balabanian. Special thanks are due to A. A. Root, editor for the Programmed Learning Project, for his criticism and helpful suggestions. Many lab instructors and students worked with the different versions of this program and helped to provide data for the necessary revisions. Their contribution is gratefully acknowledged.

C. H. Roth, Jr.
The University of Texas at Austin

CONTENTS

INTRODUCTION

This text is divided into nine parts. Four of these parts are for preparation outside of the laboratory, and the other four parts are used in the lab working with the oscilloscope. In Preparation Part I and Laboratory Part I, you will learn the relation between voltages applied at the scope terminals and the pattern which will be displayed on the screen. Part II covers displaying waveforms on the scope as a function of time. You will learn how to make accurate measurements with the scope in Preparation Part III and Lab Part III. Measurement of the phase angle between sinusoidal voltages is covered in Part IV. Part V is intended for review after you have completed the programmed instruction in the other parts.

Objectives

1. When you complete this programmed text you should be able to use the scope effectively in future laboratory work. Effective use of the scope includes the ability to:

    (a) Avoid damage to the scope.
    (b) Properly adjust and calibrate the scope.
    (c) Connect the scope to the circuit with minimum disturbance to the quantity being observed.
    (d) Display a waveform (or a selected portion thereof) and measure its characteristics (amplitude, period, frequency).
    (e) Determine the relationships between two waveforms such as phase shift.
    (f) Display x-y plots.
    (g) Interpret the results of oscilloscope measurements taking the limitations of the scope into account.

2. You should understand the operation of the scope in the sense that you are able to:

    (a) Explain the functions of the controls and input terminals and their relationship to the trace (using a simple block diagram if necessary).
    (b) Given the input signals and control settings, sketch the sweep waveform which is generated within the scope.
    (c) Given the input signals and control settings, predict the trace which will appear on the screen.
    (d) Given a desired trace, determine the necessary input signals and control settings.

Read the following instructions carefully before proceeding:

1. This programmed text is divided into frames. Each frame will ask a question or require you to take some action. The answer to each frame is given on the following page.

2. Read each frame carefully. Then write your answer(s) in the space provided or take the appropriate action. If you cannot answer the question, leave the space blank.

3. After you have written your answer(s), turn the page and check your answer(s). Most of the time you will be correct.

4. If your answer is wrong or if you left it blank, go back and correct it. Mark the incorrect frame with an X so you can review it later. Do not go on until you understand why your answer was wrong; ask your instructor for help if necessary.

5. Continue through the program frame by frame as described above. After completing each part, go back and review any frames which you missed the first time through.

6. Avoid the temptation to look at the correct answer before you write your own answer. Effective learning will occur only if you carefully study each frame and then write your own answer.

7. You will not be graded on your answers. You will "cheat" only yourself if you copy the answers instead of working them out.

8. This program is intended for individual instruction. Each student should schedule time on the oscilloscope so that he can work alone.

9. Each part is divided into several sections as indicated in the table of contents for that part. Plan your study time so that you can complete a given section at one sitting. Take your breaks in between sections. For example, for Preparation Part I, the best time to take a break is after frame 1.22 or 1.36.

10. To complete the program, you must work through the following pages four times--once for each of the four parts. Frames for Part I are found on the top half of the right-hand pages; frames for Part II on the bottom half. Similarly, frames for Parts III and IV are at the top and bottom of the left-hand pages.

11. The preparation for each part should be completed before going to lab. Before you start the lab work, your lab instructor or supervisor will check to see that you have completed the preparation and will answer any questions which you might have.

PREPARATION   PART I

1.1 This part must be completed <u>before</u> going to lab. Before proceeding, read the instructions on p. 2 if you have not already done so.

The oscilloscope is an electronic measuring instrument which displays electrical signals in graphic form. It is probably the most widely-used electronic instrument because it can be used to observe waveforms as well as measure voltage, time, frequency, and phase angle.

In this part of the program you will learn the relation between the voltages applied at the oscilloscope terminals and the pattern which is displayed on the screen.

TURN TO FRAME 1.2 ON PAGE 5

PREPARATION   PART II

2.1 In this part of the program you will learn how to display waveforms on the scope as a function of time.

<u>Displaying Waveforms as a Function of Time</u>

In this and the following frames, assume that the vertical and horizontal sensitivities are $S_v = S_h = 1$ volt/div. Also assume that the spot is centered at the left edge of the grid when no inputs are present. Thus the point $x = 0$, $y = 0$ will be at the center of the left edge of the grid.

It is desired that the spot move at a uniform rate from point A to point B in 4 seconds. Plot the required input voltages v_v and v_h as functions of time.

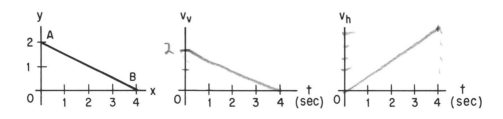

FIG. 2-1

PREPARATION PART III

3.1 In order to use the scope to make accurate measurements, the scope must be properly calibrated, and the circuit being tested must not be affected when the scope is connected to it. We will now consider the effect of measuring instruments on the quantity being measured.

<u>Measurement Errors Due to Loading</u>

An <u>ideal</u> measuring instrument does not disturb the circuit to which it is connected in any way. In other words, all the voltages and currents in a circuit are the same regardless of whether the ideal instrument is connected to the circuit or not.

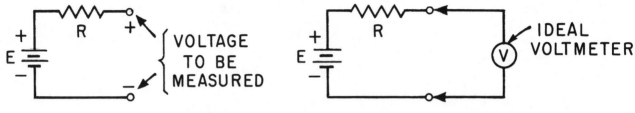

If an <u>ideal</u> voltmeter is connected as shown, the current flowing in

the circuit is _____. The ideal voltmeter will read   (a)

_____. The input impedance of the ideal voltmeter   (b)

is _____.   (c)

PREPARATION PART IV

4.1 In this section we will learn two methods of determining the phase difference between two sinusoidal voltages, the triggered sweep method and the ellipse method. In the triggered sweep method, the scope is triggered with one waveform while the other is being observed.

Given two sinusoidal voltages, we can always choose the time origin so that the phase angle associated with one of them is O. Therefore, we will assume that the given voltages are of the form

$$v_1 = A \sin \omega t \qquad \text{and } v_2 = B \sin (\omega t + \theta)$$

The voltage with O phase angle (v_1) will be referred to as the reference voltage. The phase angle of v_2, θ, is then the phase difference between the two voltages. Our problem is to measure θ. We will first review how to determine θ by inspection of a plot of v_1 and v_2.

<u>Deflection of the Electron Beam</u>

The oscilloscope displays electrical signals on the screen of a
<u>cathode-ray tube.</u> (The picture tube in a TV set is one type of
cathode-ray tube.) As shown in Fig. 1-2, the evacuated glass envelope of the cathode-ray tube contains a(an) _____ _____ (a)
which produces an electron beam, and _____ _____ (b)
which can be used to deflect the electron beam.

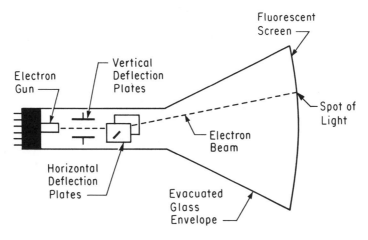

FIG. 1-2. CATHODE RAY TUBE

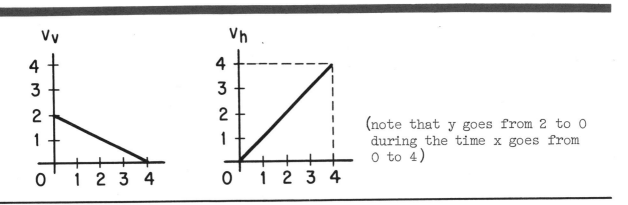

(note that y goes from 2 to 0
during the time x goes from
0 to 4)

2.2 After reaching point B (Fig. 2-1), we want the spot to jump back to point
A and then retrace the line from A to B at the same rate as before. This
action should be repeated twice more (four times in all). Sketch the required input voltages v_v and v_h.

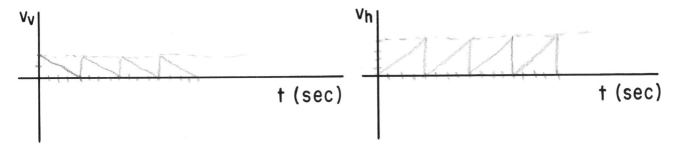

(a) zero   (b) E   (c) infinite

(Since no current was flowing before connecting the meter, we want no current to flow after connecting the meter. Therefore the ideal meter must act like an open circuit and have an infinite input impedance.)

3.2 A non-ideal voltmeter has a finite input impedance. It will draw some current from the circuit being tested and may change the voltage being measured.

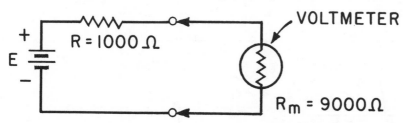

(R$_m$ represents the input impedance of the voltmeter.)

In the above circuit, the voltmeter will read _____. (a)
The voltmeter reading is less than the correct value because the voltmeter loads down the circuit. The per cent error in the voltage reading due to loading is _____. The error due to loading (b)
would be negligible only if the impedance of the voltmeter, R$_m$, is _____ than R. (c)

Determination of Phase Angle

4.2 The plot below shows $v_2 = B \sin(\omega t + \theta)$. From the equation, at t = 0, v_2 = _____. (a)

— If t = 0 here, θ = _____ degrees. (b)

— If t = 0 here, θ = _____ degrees. (c)

— If t = 0 here, θ = _____ degrees. (d)

— If t = 0 here, θ = _____ degrees. (e)

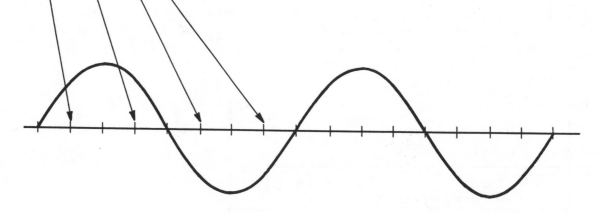

Answers to frame 1.2:   (a) electron gun
                         (b) (vertical and horizontal) deflection
                              plates

1.3 The screen is coated with a phosphor which produces a spot of light
     when the _____ _____ strikes it. Varying the   (a)
     intensity of the electron beam will cause a corresponding variation
     in the intensity of the _____.   (b)

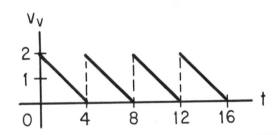 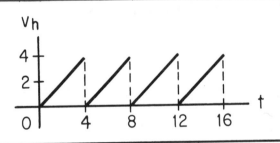

2.3 In the frames which follow, still asume that the spot is centered at the
     left edge of the grid when no inputs are present and $S_v = S_h = 1$ volt/div.

It is desired that the spot trace out
a triangle on the screen as shown. The
position of the spot at t = 0, 1 ms,
2 ms, and 3 ms is indicated. Plot the
required input voltages v_v and v_h as a
function of time.

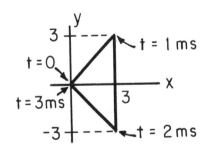

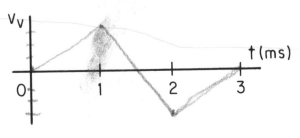 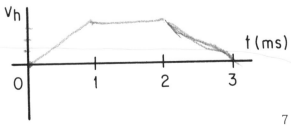

7

(a)   .9E   (b)   10%   (c)   much greater

3.3

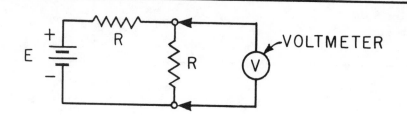

If the meter is ideal, it will read _____.   (a)

If the meter is non-ideal it will load down the circuit. When calculating the effect of loading on a circuit, first replace the circuit seen at the meter terminals by its Thevenin's equivalent:

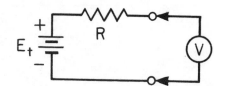

E_t = _____   (b)

R_t = _____   (c)

If the meter has an input impedance R_m it will read _____   (d)
(express your answer in terms of E_t, R_t and R_m)

(a) $v_2 = B \sin \theta$ (b)   45   (c)   135   (d)   -135 (or + 225)
(e)   -45 (or +315)

4.3   In this and the following frames, when we write an expression of the
form $v_2 = B \sin(\omega t + \theta)$ we will assume that B is positive and we
will choose the magnitude of θ to be less than or equal to 180°.
Thus instead of writing $\theta = 280°$, we will use the equivalent value
θ = _____, and instead of 190° we will use   (a)

_____.   (b)

Given: $v_2(t) = B \sin(\omega t + \theta)$

If v_2 is positive at t = 0, the sign of θ is _____.   (c)

If v_2 is negative at t = 0, the sign of θ is _____.   (d)

Given a plot of $v_2(t)$, how can we tell the sign of θ?

_____

_____   (e)

8

(a)   electron beam
(b)   spot (of light)

1.4   When the electron beam strikes the screen, it produces heat as well
as light. If a high-intensity spot is left stationary on the screen
for a period of time, the screen will be overheated and a burned spot
will result. This causes permanent damage to the cathode-ray tube.
Damage to the cathode-ray tube screen may be avoided by

keeping the intensity _____ when the spot is stationary   (a)

keeping the spot _____ when the intensity is high.   (b)

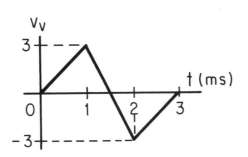

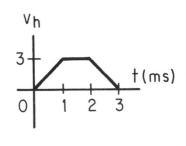

2.4   The picture traced out in frame 2.3 would fade out as soon as the input
signals were over. In order to observe a steady picture on the scope
screen, it would be necessary to retrace the figure on the screen periodically. This could be accomplished by _____
_____

(a) E/2   (b) E/2   (c) R/2

(d) $E_t \dfrac{R_m}{R_m + R_t}$

3.4 A voltmeter is used to measure the output voltage of a network as shown.

The Thevenin's equivalent of the network is

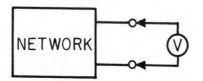 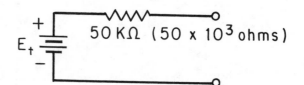

The meter reads 9.5 volts and has an input impedance of 1 megohm $(10^6$ ohms$)$.

What would an ideal voltmeter read? _____ (a)

What is the per cent error due to loading? _____ (b)

(Per cent error is defined as $\dfrac{\text{error}}{\text{correct value}}$ x 100%.)

(a) -80°   (b) -170°   (c) positive   (d) negative

(e) The sign of θ is the same as the sign of v_2 at t = 0.

4.4 $v_2(t) = B \sin(\omega t + \theta)$ is plotted below for two values of θ.

In both cases, the sign of θ is _____. (a)

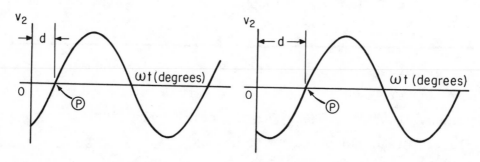

The "0° point" on the sine wave (that point at which a full cycle of the sine wave starts) is labeled P. At point P, $\omega t + \theta =$ _____ (b)

so $\theta =$ _____. (c)

For the case where θ is negative, if the distance between the origin and the "0° point" on the sine wave is d (in degrees),

$\theta =$ _____ (d)

(a) low (turned down)
(b) moving (in motion)

☐ **1.5** When no voltage is applied to either set of deflection plates, the
electron beam passes straight through between the plates and produces
a spot on the center of the screen.

Now consider the effect of applying a voltage between the vertical
deflection plates. If the top plate (see below) is made positive
with respect to the bottom plate, the negatively-charged electrons
are attracted toward the (top/bottom) _____ plate and the   (a)
beam is deflected (upward/downward)_____   (b)

If the right horizontal deflection plate is made positive with respect to the left plate, the spot on the screen will be deflected to
the _____.   (c)

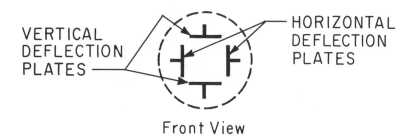

Front View

---

repeating the input signals periodically

☐ **2.5** The following waveform is applied to the vertical input:

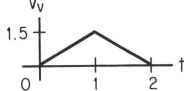

We wish to trace out the same waveform on the scope face:

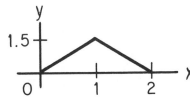

Sketch the waveform which must be applied to the horizontal amplifier
input.

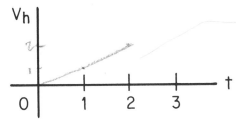

(a) $\dfrac{10^6 E_t}{50 \times 10^3 + 10^6} = 9.5$ $E_t = 9.5 \times 1.05 \approx \underline{10}$

(b) $\dfrac{10 - 9.5}{10} \times 100\% = \underline{5\%}$

3.5 Now consider a measuring instrument whose input circuit is a capacitor.

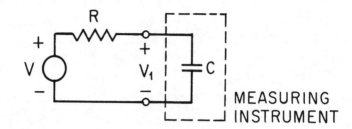

If V is a DC source, the capacitor acts like a(n) _____ cir- (a)
cuit, so the input voltage to the measuring instrument is _____. (b)
If V is an AC source, for very high frequencies the capacitor approaches a(n) _____ circuit, so the input voltage to the (c)
measuring instrument approaches _____. (d)

(a) negative   (b) 0   (c) -ωt   (d) -d

4.5 $v_2 = B \sin(\omega t + \theta)$ is plotted below for two values of θ.
In each case, give the value of θ.

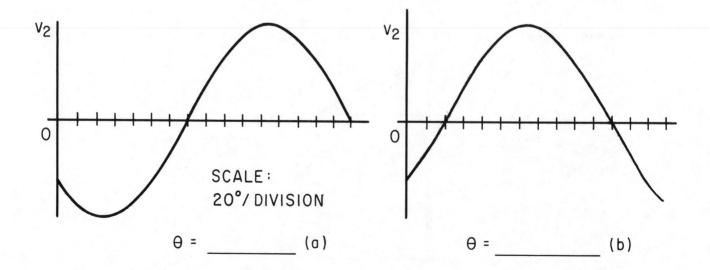

SCALE:
20°/ DIVISION

θ = _____ (a)   θ = _____ (b)

12

1.6 When the input signals are connected directly to the deflection plates, a
large voltage is required to deflect the spot a small amount (in the order
of 20 volts for one centimeter deflection). In order to observe small
signals, these signals must be amplified before being applied to the deflection plates as shown in Fig. 1-6. Each amplifier multiplies its input
voltage by a positive constant.

In Fig. 1-6, if v_v is positive the _____ plate will be positive   (a)

with respect to the _____ plate.   (b)

If v_h is positive the _____ plate will be positive with respect   (c)

to the _____ plate.   (d)

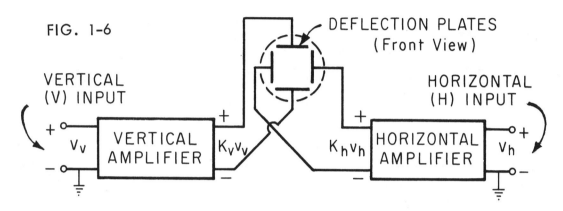

FIG. 1-6

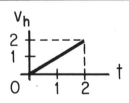

2.6 If the vertical input is periodic and we wish to observe a single
period on the scope, we could trace out a single period of the waveform only once on the scope screen; however, this picture would fade
out immediately and would be difficult to observe. We can obtain a
steady picture by retracing the same waveform over and over again.
To do this, we must apply a periodic sweep waveform to the horizontal
amplifier input. If v_v and v_h are as shown, the maximum horizontal

deflection is _____ div. Sketch the trace which appears on   (a)
the screen. (S_v and S_h are still 1 volt/div.)   (b)

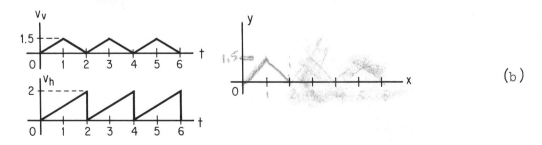

(a) open   (b) V   (c) short   (d) 0

3.6   If V is an AC source, the loading
effect of the capacitor on V_1 will
depend on the frequency.

In terms of ω and C, the magnitude
of the impedance of the capacitor
is _____ (a)

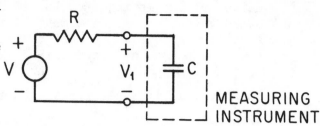

Therefore, as the frequency increases, the impedance of the
capacitor will (increase/
decrease) _____ (b)

and the voltage measured by the
measuring instrument will
_____ . (c)

If the magnitude of V remains
constant, make a rough sketch of
the magnitude of V_1 as a function of frequency.

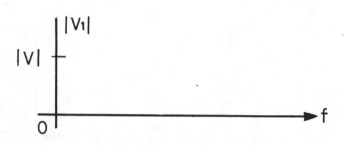

(a) -140°   (b) -40°

4.6   Now consider the case where the phase angle is positive. If the waveform starts at t = 0, the "0° point" on the sine wave will not be
visible. Imagine the sine wave extended back to where it crosses the
ωt axis as shown by the dotted lines on the plots below. If point P
were visible, we could read the value of θ directly off the plot as
indicated. Since P will not be visible, we must compute θ indirectly.
The "180° point" on the sine wave is labeled Q. In terms of θ, the
distance between the origin and Q is _____ .   (a)

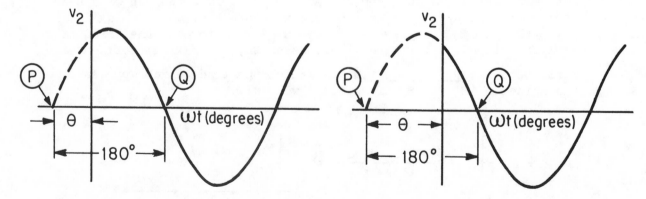

For the case where θ is positive, if the distance between the origin
and the "180° point" on the sine wave is d (in degrees), θ = _____ .   (b)

14

(a) top   (b) bottom   (c) right   (d) left
     (upper)   (lower)

1.7   In Fig. 1-6, if the vertical input voltage is negative, the spot on
the screen will be deflected _____. To deflect the spot   (a)
to the right, a _____ voltage must be applied to the   (b)   .
_____ input.   (c)

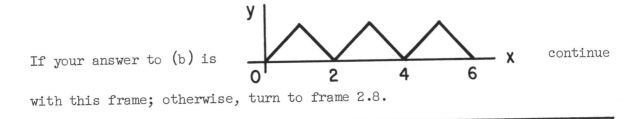

If your answer to (b) is   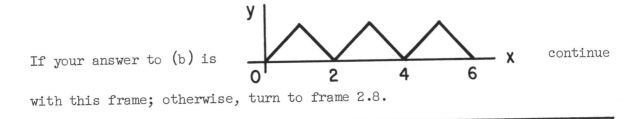   continue

with this frame; otherwise, turn to frame 2.8.

2.7   In frame 2.6 the horizontal signal is

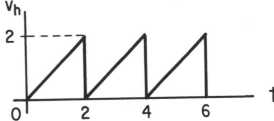

Since the peak value of v_h is 2, and we have assumed a horizontal sensitivity of 1 volt/div, the maximum horizontal deflection is _____2_____ div.
Now, the maximum horizontal deflection in your answer is 6 div., so it
can't be right. Go back to frame 2.6 and try again.

(a) $1/\omega C$

(b) decrease

(c) decrease

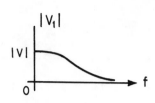

3.7 We will now consider the loading effect of the scope on the circuit being measured. When the input switch is set to DC, the input impedance of the vertical amplifier of the scope can be represented by

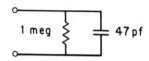

For DC voltages, the input impedance is _____   (a)

As the frequency is increased, the input impedance will _____   (b)
because of the shunt capacitance.

At very high frequencies, the impedance of the shunt capacitor becomes much less than 1 megohm, and practically all of the input current will flow through the capacitor. At such high frequencies, the
input circuit of the scope amplifier can be approximately represented
by a _____ of numerical value   (c)
_____.   (d)

(a) $180° - \theta$ (b) $180° - d$

4.7 For each of the following plots, give the value of the phase angle:

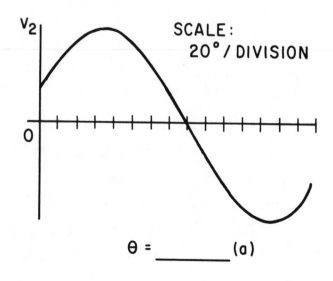

SCALE:
20°/ DIVISION

$\theta =$ _____ (a)

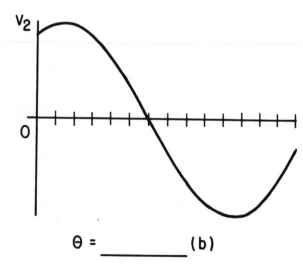

$\theta =$ _____ (b)

(a) downward   (b) positive   (c) horizontal

1.8 The inputs to the vertical and horizontal amplifiers (labeled v_v and v_h in Fig. 1-6) are brought out to terminals on the front of the scope as shown in Fig. 1-8. Voltage sources are connected to these input terminals with the polarities shown. The spot will appear in the _____ quadrant of the scope screen. (Remember that the polarity markings on v_v and v_h are reference polarities and do not necessarily correspond to the actual polarity of the applied voltage.)

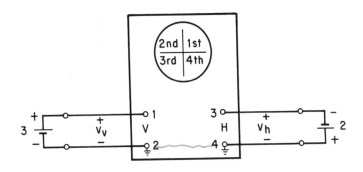

FIG. 1-8

Answers to 2.6:

(a) 2 div.   (b)

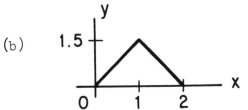

(Note that the waveform is retraced 3 times; it is not repeated.)

2.8 Generating the Sweep Waveform

If a signal $v_v(t)$ is applied to the vertical scope input and we wish to display v_v as a function of time, we must provide a horizontal signal of the type discussed in the preceding frames. The required horizontal signal is generated within the scope by the TIME BASE. To display v_v as a function of time, indicate the proper position of the horizontal display switch by drawing a line on Fig. 5-3 (p. 211).   (a)

The two main parts of the TIME BASE are the TRIGGER PULSE GENERATOR and the SWEEP GENERATOR as shown in Fig. 5-4. When the scope is used to display a waveform as a function of time the output of the sweep generator is connected to the ____horizontal____ amplifier.   (b)
Which scope input is not used? ____external horiz. input____   (c)

(a) 1 megohm   (b) decreases

(c) capacitor (the resistor can be omitted since practically all of the input current flows through the capacitor at high frequencies)

(d) 47 pf

3.8 Draw an equivalent circuit which represents the input impedance of the vertical amplifier of the scope. Specify values for both components.

(a)

Draw an equivalent circuit which represents the input impedance of the scope for DC voltages.

(b)

Draw an equivalent circuit which approximately represents the input impedance of the scope for very high frequencies.

(c)

(a) 20°   (b) 60°

4.8 Sketch the following waveforms:

(a) $v_2 = 10 \sin (\omega t + 140°)$
(b) $v_3 = 10 \sin (\omega t - 140°)$

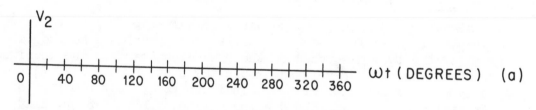

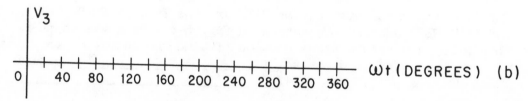

Check to see that your waveforms cross the ωt axis when $(\omega t + \theta) = 0, 180°, 360°$, etc. Also check to see that your plots have the proper sign at $t = 0$.

2nd (since v_v is + and v_h is -)

Grounding

1.9 The ground symbol (⏚) which appears in Figs. 1-6 and 1-8 indicates
that one vertical input terminal and one horizontal input terminal
are "grounded," i.e., are connected to the scope case and chassis.
(The chassis has the electronic components mounted on it and serves
as a common electrical connection for many of the scope circuits.)

On Fig. 1-8 draw a line between two terminals which are connected
directly together through the scope case and chassis.   (a)

Give the voltage between each of the following terminal pairs in
Fig. 1-8:

V_{12} = _____ 3 _____ V_{34} = _____ -5 _____ V_{24} = _____ 0 _____   (bcd)

V_{13} = _____ 1 _____ V_{14} = _____ +3 _____ V_{32} = _____ -2 _____   (efg)

NOTE: V_{12} means the voltage drop from 1 to 2, etc.

(a) switch is connected to TIME BASE   (b) horizontal

(c) external horizontal input

2.9 The SWEEP GENERATOR output is 0 until it is triggered by a pulse at the input. If a trigger pulse occurs, the following sweep waveform is generated
at the output:

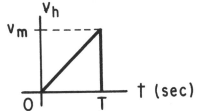

Assume that the peak voltage, v_m, is just sufficient to deflect the spot
the full width of the screen. If a single trigger pulse occurs at the
input of the sweep generator, describe the horizontal motion of the spot
on the screen. (Include the time T in your answer.)

Since v_m is positive it trave left to right across
screen in T sec once and return to same spot.

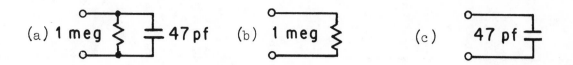

(a) 1 meg ⌇ ⊣⊢ 47 pf   (b) 1 meg ⌇   (c) 47 pf ⊣⊢

3.9 When the vertical amplifier input switch is set to AC, there is a blocking capacitor in series with the vertical amplifier input. However, the effect of this blocking capacitor on the input impedance is negligible except at very low frequencies.

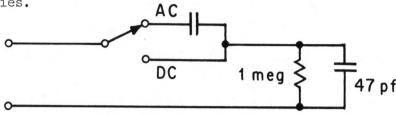

Over the frequency range where the AC input is normally used, should there be any significant difference between the input impedance with the switch set to AC and with the switch set to DC? _____

Why? _____

_____

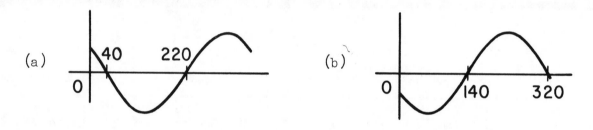

(a) 40   220   0

(b) 0   140   320

4.9 If $v_2 = 5 \sin(\omega t + \theta)$, complete the following table:

range of θ	$0° < \theta < 90°$	$90° < \theta < 180°$	$-180° < \theta < -90°$	$-90° < \theta < 0°$	
sign of $v_2(0)$					(a)
sketch of v_2					(b)

In which case is there a positive peak of the sine wave between the

origin and the first time the curve crosses the time axis? _____ (c)

A negative peak? _____ (d)

(a) ⌐ V   H ⌐
    │ o   o │
    │ ⏚   ⏚│

(b) $V_{12} = +3$ (c) $V_{34} = -2$ (d) $V_{24} = 0$

(e) $V_{13} = +5$ (f) $V_{14} = +3$ (g) $V_{32} = -2$

1.10 A resistor and battery are connected to the ground terminals of the
scope as shown below. What is the current flowing through the resistor (if any) ? _____ $I = E/R$ _____ What is the voltage be-   (a)
tween terminals 2 and 4 ? _____ 0 _____   (b)

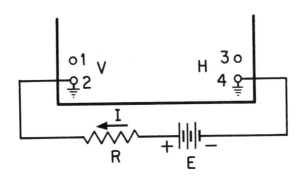

The spot will move across the screen once (at a uniform rate) in
T seconds and then return to its starting point.

2.10 The rate at which the spot sweeps across the screen is variable by
means of the TIME/DIV (SWEEP TIME/CM) switch. The screen is 10
divisions wide. If the sweep rate is set at 50 msec/div, the time
required for the spot to cross the screen once will be

_____ 500 ms _____ .   (a)

If the sweep rate is set to R sec/div, the time required for the
spot to travel x div is

t = _____ (R sec/div)(x div) _____   (b)

No, because the impedance of the blocking capacitor is negligible over the frequency range where the AC input is normally used.

3.10 | The vertical amplifier is set to DC and S_v = 1 volt/div, and the input is connected as shown. The deflection of the spot is

_____ divisions. If the scope were an ideal measuring (a)

instrument, the deflection would be _____ divisions. (b)

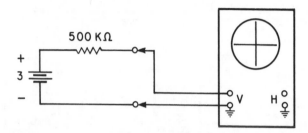

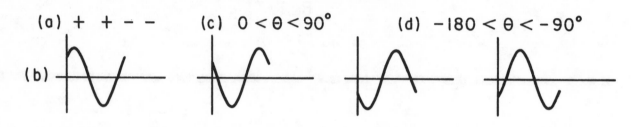

(a) + + - -

(c) $0 < \theta < 90°$

(d) $-180 < \theta < -90°$

(b)

Phase Shift Measurement by the Triggered Sweep Method

4.10 | The scope is set to _internal_ trigger with trigger slope set to + and trigger level set so that the sweep triggers when the input voltage goes through 0. The applied vertical input voltage is v = 10 sin $(\omega t + \theta)$. Sketch the waveform which will be observed on the screen, paying particular attention to the point at which the waveform starts.

(a)

Does the picture observed depend on the value of θ? _____ (b)

Explain why or why not _____ (c)

Can we determine the value of θ by observing the waveform and using

internal trigger? _____ (d)

22

(a) E/R (since the ground terminals are connected together internally)

(b) 0

1.11 If sources are connected to the scope terminals as shown below, indicate a possible location for the spot on the diagram.

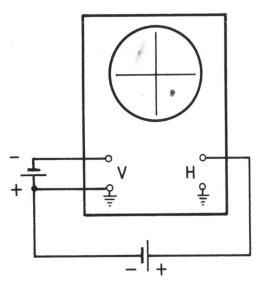

(a) 500 ms (1/2 sec)   (b) t = (R sec/div) · (x div)

2.11 If the sweep rate is set so that the spot will take 3 seconds to cross the screen and the sweep generator is triggered once at t = 1, sketch the sweep waveform which will be generated.

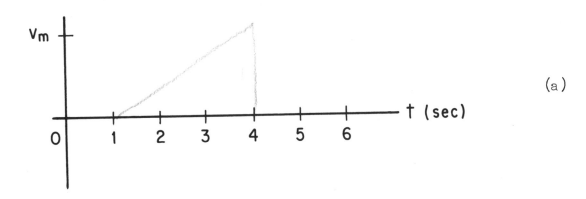

(a)

For the above example, the sweep rate is _____,3_____ sec/div.   (b)

(a) 2 (since the input voltage is $\dfrac{1 \text{ meg}}{.5 \text{ meg} + 1 \text{ meg}}$ 3 = 2)

(b) 3

Use of the Scope Probe to Reduce Loading

3.11 The deflection is less than the correct value because the scope loads down
the circuit. How could the loading effect of the scope be decreased?

_____

If your answer to 4.10(b) is YES, continue with this frame. Otherwise,
turn to frame 4.12.

4.11 When _internal_ trigger is used the sweep is triggered by the vertical
input voltage. Since the trigger level is set to O, the value of the
input voltage when the sweep triggers will be _____.
Therefore, the waveform will start when the input voltage is

_____. Now turn back to 4.10 and try again.

anywhere in the 4th quadrant

1.12 The following voltages are desired at the scope input terminals:

vertical input voltage (v_v) = +3 volts

horizontal input voltage (v_h) = -3 volts

The arrangement shown below is proposed. Will it provide the required voltages? ___No___ (a)

If not, explain. ___INPUTS ARE GROUNDED___ (b)

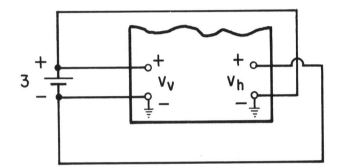

(a) 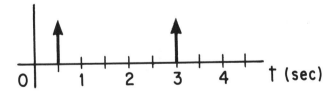   (b) $\dfrac{3 \text{ sec}}{10 \text{ div}}$ = .3 sec/div

---

2.12 If the sweep rate is set at .1 sec/div and the trigger pulse input to the sweep generator is as follows

Sketch the sweep waveform which will be generated.

If you need a hint, look at Fig. 5-4 on p. 211.

25

3.12 A probe* is available to increase the effective input impedance of the scope. The probe also attenuates (reduces) the input signal so that the deflection is less for a given input and sensitivity setting.

If a probe which has a DC impedance of 9 megohms is connected to the scope input as shown, the effective DC input impedance of the scope (including the probe) is _____. (a)

If a DC voltage of V_p volts is applied to the input terminals of the probe, the voltage at the scope input terminals would be _____. (b)
This probe attenuates a DC input signal by a factor of _____. (c)

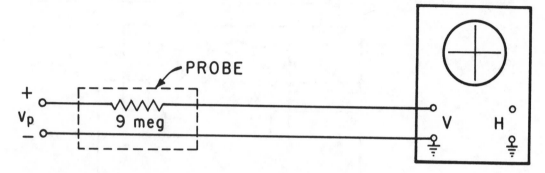

*In this and subsequent frames, the word probe will refer to a 10X attenuating probe.

Answers to 4.10:

(a)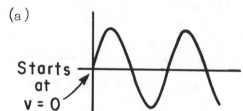

Starts at v = 0

(b) NO

(c) the waveform starts when v = 0 and has a positive slope since that is when the sweep triggers

(d) NO

TURN TO FRAME 4.12

(a) If your answer is YES, continue with this frame. Otherwise, turn to
frame 1.14.

| 1.13 | Yes would be the correct answer <u>if</u> the ground terminals were independent.

The voltage between the ground terminals on the scope is always _____ (a)

because _____ (b)

Now turn back to fram 1.12 and try again.

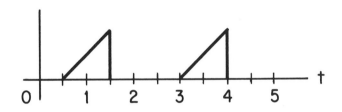

(Note that the duration
of the sweep waveform
is .1 sec/div x 10 div=
1 sec.)

| 2.13 | If a periodic waveform is used as a triggering signal, the sweep is
triggered periodically. For the following sweep waveform the sweep
is triggered once every __3 secs__. The spot is at the left edge (a)
of the screen (x = 0) between t = __2__ and ____3____,
t = __5__ and __6__, etc. The sweep rate is (b)
____.2____ sec/div. (Assume that v_m is just sufficient to deflect (c)
the spot the full screen width of 10 divisions.)

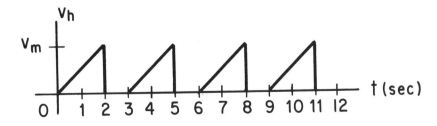

(a) 10 megohms (9 megohms from the probe and 1 megohm from the scope)

(b) $V_p/10$　　(c) 10

3.13　The probe is now connected to the same source as was used in frame 3.10 (see below). To compensate for the probe attenuation, we will use $S_v = 0.1$ volt/div instead of 1 volt/div. The voltage at the probe input terminals (V_p) is _____. The voltage at the scope input　(a)
terminals is _____. Since $S_v = 0.1$ volt/div, the deflection　(b)
of the spot is _____. Compare this with frame 3.10 and　(c)
note that the loading effect is reduced when the probe is used.

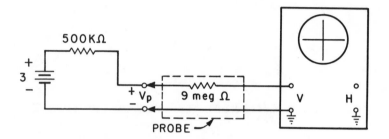

4.12　(1) The scope is set on internal trigger. $v_1 = \sin \omega t$ is applied to the vertical input and the trigger slope and level controls are adjusted to obtain the picture shown in Fig. 4.12a.

(2) With the scope controls still set as in (1) above, the vertical input is changed to $v_2 = \sin (\omega t + 45°)$. (Remember that the scope is still set on _internal_ trigger.) The resulting trace will be as shown in Fig. 4.12 (a/b/c) _____　(a)

(3) With the vertical input still $v_2 = \sin (\omega t + 45°)$, $v_1 = \sin \omega t$ is applied to the external trigger input, and the trigger source is switched to _external_. The resulting trace would be as shown in Fig. 4.12 _____. Explain. _____　(b)

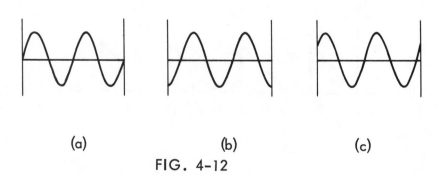

(a)　　　　　(b)　　　　　(c)

FIG. 4-12

Answers to 1.12:

    (a) NO is the correct answer.

    (b) The battery is shorted out by the internal connection between the ground terminals.

Deflection of the Spot by DC Inputs

1.14 The scope screen has grid lines superimposed on it so that the amount of deflection is easy to observe. In the diagram below, the vertical deflection of the spot is

_____ divisions (a)

and the horizontal deflec-

tion of the spot is

_____ divisions   (b)

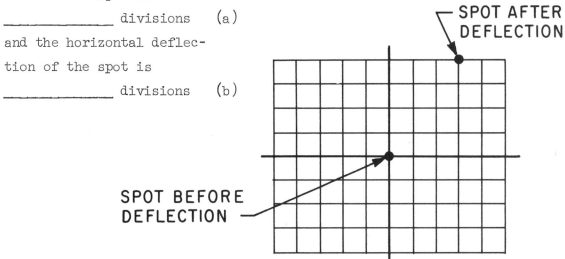

    (a) 3 sec   (b) 2 and 3, 5 and 6, etc.   (c) .2 sec/div

2.14 Once the sweep generator has been triggered, it cannot be retriggered until the sweep is completed. If a trigger pulse occurs during the middle of a sweep waveform, this trigger pulse will have no effect. In the following diagram, what will be the effect of a trigger pulse which occurs at $t = t_2$? _____nothing_____ At $t = t_3$?   (a)

_____nothing_____ At $t = t_4$? _____new sweep triggered again_____   (b,c)

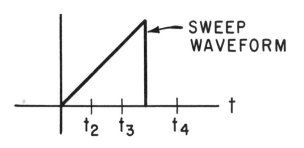

29

(a) $3 \dfrac{10M}{10M + .5M}$ = 2.86 volts   (b) $\dfrac{2.86}{10}$ = .286 volts

(c) $\dfrac{.286}{.1}$ = 2.86 div. (compared with 2 without the probe)

$\boxed{3.14}$ We have seen how a probe could be used to raise the input impedance of
the scope and reduce the loading for DC (or low frequency) signals.
We will now turn our attention to high frequencies. At high frequencies the input impedance of the scope looks like a capacitor. In
order to reduce the capacitive loading due to the scope, we must

(increase/decrease) _____ the input impedance. Since   (a)

the magnitude of the input impedance is $1/\omega C$, we must _____   (b)

the input capacitance. This can be accomplished by placing another

capacitor in (series/parallel) _____ with the scope   (c)

input capacitance.

(a)   a (since the scope still triggers when the level is 0 and the
       slope is +)

(b)   c. The scope now triggers at t = 0 so the waveform begins at
       $v_2 = \sin 45°$.

$\boxed{4.13}$ We have two voltage sources $v_1 = A \sin \omega t$ and $v_2 = B \sin (\omega t + \theta)$.
Before we display v_2 on the screen, we must determine the location of
the origin (t = 0). To locate the origin, we will first display v_1
and adjust the triggering controls to obtain the picture shown at
the bottom of the page. Label the horizontal axis with the appro-   (a)
priate number of degrees at each division.

Next we will connect v_2 to the vertical input. In order to maintain
the origin (t = 0) at the same point on the screen, we must set the
trigger source to _____ and trigger the sweep with   (b)
_____. Sketch the resulting trace when $\theta = -120°$.   (c)

(d)

30

(a) 4   (b) 3

1.15 The vertical deflection, y, is proportional to the
vertical input voltage, v_v. The amount of deflection obtained for a given v_v depends on the vertical
sensitivity. The sensitivity is defined as the
number of volts required to deflect the spot one
division. If the vertical sensitivity is S_v volts/
division and vertical input is v_v volts, the vertical deflection of the spot is y = _____
divisions. Make sure your answer is dimensionally
correct.

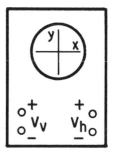

(a) No effect   (b) No effect   (c) the sweep will be triggered again

---

2.15 If the sweep rate is set at .5 sec/div and the trigger pulse input to the
sweep generator is as follows:

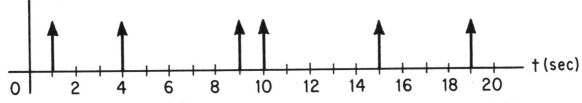

plot the horizontal (x) deflection of the spot as a function of time:

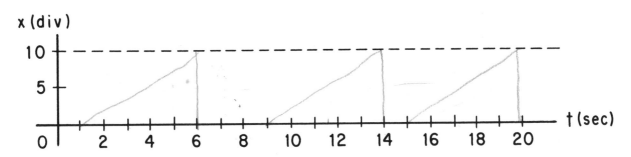

(a) increase (since the loading effect is less when the input impedance is high)
(b) decrease
(c) series (series capacitors combine like parallel resistors)

3.15 Let us consider how a voltage divides across two capacitors in series. (Assume that the capacitors are initially uncharged.)

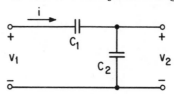

If a current i flows in the series combination:

$$v_2 = \frac{1}{C_2} \int_0^t i(t)dt$$

$$v_1 = \underline{\hspace{3cm}} + \underline{\hspace{3cm}}$$ (a)

$$\frac{v_2}{v_1} = \frac{\underline{\hspace{2cm}}}{\underline{\hspace{1cm}} + \underline{\hspace{1cm}}} = \frac{\underline{\hspace{2cm}}}{\underline{\hspace{1cm}} + \underline{\hspace{1cm}}} = \frac{\underline{\hspace{2cm}}}{\underline{\hspace{1cm}} + \underline{\hspace{1cm}}}$$ (b)

Does the voltage ratio depend on the frequency of the waveform of i? _____ (c)

If your answer to 4.13b is _internal_, continue with this frame. Otherwise, turn to frame 4.15.

4.14 If the scope is set to INTERNAL trigger, the trigger SLOPE is +, the trigger LEVEL is 0, and the vertical input is $v_2 = B \sin(\omega t + \theta)$, the sweep will trigger when $v_2 = \underline{\hspace{2cm}}$. (Your answer must be independent of θ.)

We want the sweep to trigger when $\underline{t = 0}$ instead of when $v_2 = 0$. When $t = 0$, $v_1 = A \sin \omega t = 0$. Therefore, when we are observing v_2, if we want the sweep to trigger when $t = 0$, should we use v_1 or v_2 as our source of triggering voltage? _____

Now turn back to frame 4.13 and try again.

1.16 | If the vertical gain is set at 5 volts/div, an input voltage of 10 volts will deflect the spot <u>upward</u> _____ divisions.   (a)

To deflect the spot 3 divisions <u>downward</u>, an input voltage of _____ volts is required.   (b)

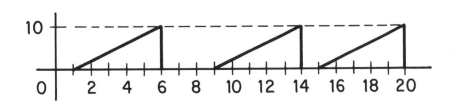

THIS IS A GOOD PLACE TO TAKE A BREAK

Trigger Slope and Level Controls

2.16 | We have just studied the operation of the sweep generator. The output of the sweep generator is used to drive the horizontal amplifier when we display a waveform on the screen as a function of time. When a trigger pulse occurs at the input of the sweep generator, a sweep waveform is generated which sweeps the spot across the screen once. When the next trigger pulse occurs, the sweep will be triggered again provided that the previous sweep has been completed.

As shown in Fig. 5-4 (p. 211) the input pulses to the sweep generator come from the _____trigger pulse generator_____. If there   (a)
is no triggering signal present at the input of the trigger pulse generator no output pulse will occur. In order to trigger the sweep generator, a _____triggering signal_____ must be   (b)
present at the input of the trigger pulse generator.

(a) $v_1 = 1/C_1 \int_0^t i(t)dt + 1/C_2 \int_0^t i(t)dt$

(b) $\dfrac{v_2}{v_1} = \dfrac{1/C_2 \int_0^t i(t)dt}{1/C_1 \int_0^t i(t)dt + 1/C_2 \int_0^t i(t)dt} = \dfrac{1/C_2}{1/C_1 + 1/C_2} = \dfrac{C_1}{C_1 + C_2}$

(c) No (The voltage ratio is independent of frequency and waveshape since i cancels out.)

3.16 Previously we used a resistive voltage divider to raise the input impedance of the scope:

The input resistance of the divider is _____ (a)

and the voltage ratio is
v_2/v_1 = _____ (b)

In a similar manner we will use a capacitive voltage divider to reduce the input capacitance. How does the frequency and waveshape of v_1 effect the voltage ratio of the divider? _____ (c)

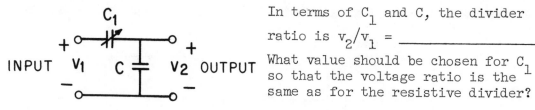

In terms of C_1 and C, the divider ratio is v_2/v_1 = _____ (d)

What value should be chosen for C_1 so that the voltage ratio is the same as for the resistive divider?

_____ (e)

With this value of C_1 the input capacitance is _____ (f)
(Remember that series capacitors combine like parallel resistors.)

Answers to 4.13:

(b) external
(c) v_1

(d)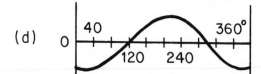

4.15 In the previous frame, each division corresponds to _____ (a) degrees. To improve the accuracy with which we can determine the phase angle, we will change the time scale so that each division corresponds to 20° After this change, sketch the waveform we whould see when the vertical input is $v_1 = A \sin \omega t$.

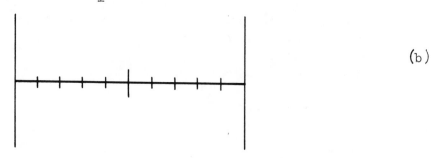

(b)

(a) $\dfrac{10 \text{ volts}}{5 \text{ volts/div}}$ = 2 div (b) -3 div x 5 volts/div = -15 volts

---

1.17 The horizontal deflection, x, is proportional to the horizontal input voltage, v_h. The gain of the horizontal amplifier determines the horizontal sensitivity, S_h, measured in volts/division. The horizontal deflection (in divisions) is given by the following expression:

$$x = \text{\underline{\hspace{5cm}}}$$

(a) trigger pulse generator

(b) triggering signal

2.17 The point on the triggering signal at which the sweep is triggered depends on the setting of two switches, TRIGGER SLOPE AND TRIGGER LEVEL. The trigger slope determines whether the sweep is triggered on the positive or negative slope of the waveform. If the TRIGGER SLOPE is negative and the triggering signal is as shown, the sweep could be triggered at some time in region ___B___ or ___D___ but not in ___A___ or ___C___ .

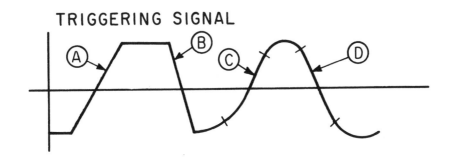

TRIGGERING SIGNAL

(a) 10R   (b) 1/10   (c) No effects   (d) $C_1/(C_1 + C)$

(e) $\dfrac{C_1}{C_1 + C} = \dfrac{1}{10}$ so $C_1 = \dfrac{C}{9}$

(f) $\dfrac{C\left(\frac{C}{9}\right)}{C + \frac{C}{9}} = \dfrac{C}{10}$

3.17 Now consider using both voltage dividers simultaneously:

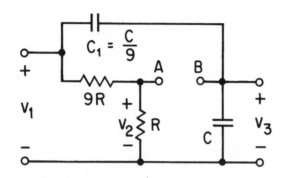

With C_1 adjusted so that $v_2 = v_3$, how much current will flow in a wire connected from A to B? _____ (a)

How will connecting a wire from A to B affect the behavior of the network?

_____ (b)

What is the voltage ratio v_2/v_1 with a wire from A to B?

_____ (c)

As the frequency of the input signal is increased, this ratio will (increase/remain constant/decrease) _____ (d)

(a) 40°   (b)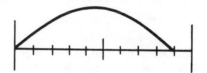

4.16 The two steps used in measurement of phase shift by the triggered sweep method are:

    (1) Calibrate the time axis (in degrees) using v_1.

    (2) Observe v_2 using the same time axis.

Once the time origin is set in step 1, the triggering circuit must not be changed in any way. Therefore, in both steps 1 and 2 the trigger source must be set to _____ and in both steps v_1 must (a)
be connected to the _____ input. (b)

In step (1), v_2 (is/is not) _____ connected to the scope, (c)
and in step (2), v_2 is connected to the _____ input. (d)

Check your own answer to make sure that it is dimensionally correct.

1.18 If the horizontal sensitivity is 0.5 volts/div, 2 volts will deflect
the spot _____ divisions to the right. How much, and in what   (a)
direction will -1.5 volts deflect the spot? _____   (b)

B or D, but not in A or C.

2.18 The TRIGGER LEVEL control is variable from - to + and determines the
value (sign and magnitude) of the triggering voltage at which the
sweep is triggered. If the TRIGGER LEVEL control is set at 0, the
sweep is triggered when the waveform passes through 0. The TRIGGER
LEVEL and SLOPE controls are adjusted so that the sweep is triggered
at point B on the waveform shown below. If we want the sweep to be
triggered at point A instead of B, we should set the TRIGGER
_____Level_____ control to _____0_____.   (a,b)

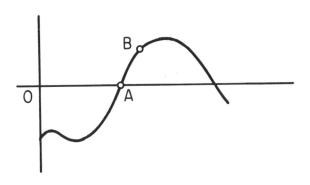

37

(a) None   (b) No effect   (c) $\frac{1}{10}$ (d) Remain Constant

---

3.18 For the same network with no connection between A and B, draw an equivalent <u>input</u> circuit consisting of one resistor and one capacitor.

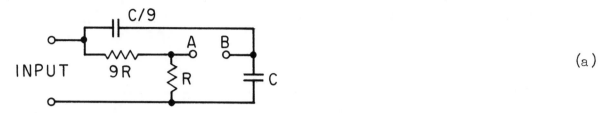

(a)

Now draw the equivalent circuit when A and B are connected (<u>one</u> R and <u>one</u> C).

(b)

(a) external (external must be used in step 2 and the setting must be the same for both steps)

(b) external trigger   (c) is not   (d) vertical

4.17 For the following network, $v_1 = A \sin \omega t$ and $v_2 = B \sin (\omega t + \theta)$. θ is to be measured by the triggered sweep method.

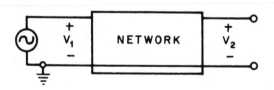

Which voltage should be observed in step 1? _____   (a)

Which voltage should be observed in step 2? _____   (b)

For both steps, the external trigger input should be _____   (c)

Why must the triggering controls be set exactly the same for both steps? _____   (d)

(a) 4   (b) 3 div. to the left.

1.19 The grid lines on the scope screen are reproduced below.

Assuming that the spot is initially centered on the screen when no voltages are applied, plot the location of the spot for each of the following conditions:

(a) $S_v = 5$ v/div, $v_v = -15$ v;

   $S_h = .1$ v/div, $v_h = .2$ v

(b) $S_v = 10$ mv/div, $v_v = 30$ mv;

   $S_h = 2$ v/div, $v_h = -4$ v

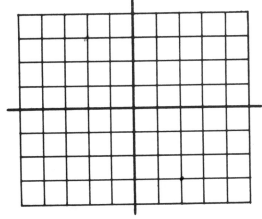

(a) LEVEL   (b) 0

2.19 A sine wave is used as a triggering signal. The resulting trigger pulses and sweep waveform are shown below:

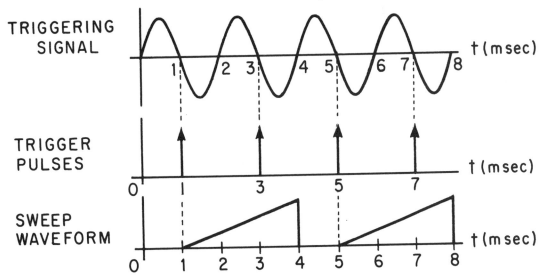

The trigger slope is set to ___. Trigger level is set to ___0___. (a,b)

Sweep time/div is set to _.3 sec/div_. The sweep generator is not (c)

triggered by pulses at t = ___3 ms___ or t = ___7 ms___ because (d)

_____. (e)

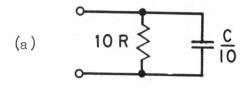

(a)

(b) the same (since connecting
A to B doesn't effect
circuit operation)

3.19 Now let's get back to the probe and the scope. If the probe contained only a resistor as shown below, as the input frequency was increased, the ratio V_v/V_p would _____ (a)

If we want V_v/V_p to be independent of frequency indicate on the diagram what must be added to the probe. If in doubt, go back and restudy frame 3.17. (b)

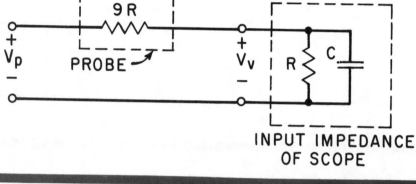

INPUT IMPEDANCE
OF SCOPE

(a) v_1　　(b) v_2　　(c) v_1　　(d) so the time origin will be the same

---

4.18 Let us review some of the rules for making connections to the scope:

The ground point on the circuit being measured should always be connected directly to the _____. (a)

If one terminal of the voltage being observed is grounded, then it is necessary to use only the _____ on the differential (b)
amplifier, but if neither terminal of the voltage being measured is grounded, both the _____ and _____ on the (c)
differential amplifier must be used.

561
ONLY

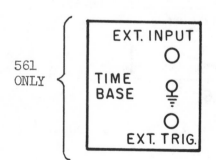

The 561 scope has two input terminals (and ground) on the time base as shown. Circle the one which (d)
should be used to trigger the sweep. If we are displaying a waveform as a function of time we can use the _____ terminal, but if (e)
we are displaying one voltage on the vertical against another voltage on the horizontal we must use the _____ terminal. (f)

(a) plot at x = 2, y = -3

(b) plot at x = -2, y = 3

1.20 The vertical and horizontal inputs to the scope are not completely independent because their ground terminals are _____

_____.

(a) - (negative)   (b) 0   (c) 0.3 msec   (d) 3 msec or 7 msec

(e) the previous sweep waveform has not gone to completion

2.20 A trigger pulse will occur at the output of the trigger pulse generator (Fig. 5-4) provided that two conditions are met:

(a) the ____slope____ of the triggering signal matches the
     setting of the __(TRIGGER) SLOPE__ control and   (a)

(b) the ____level____ of the triggering signal matches the
     setting of the __(TRIGGER) LEVEL__ control.   (b)

The trigger pulse will then trigger the sweep generator provided
that ____the last sweep has been completed____   (c)

41

(a) decrease

(b)

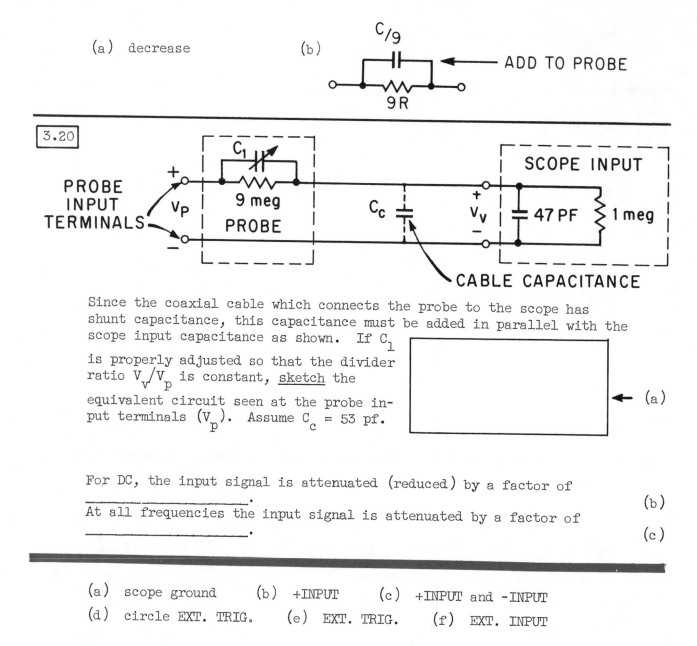

$C/9$ ADD TO PROBE

$9R$

3.20

PROBE INPUT TERMINALS

V_P

C_1

9 meg

PROBE

C_c

CABLE CAPACITANCE

V_v

SCOPE INPUT

47 PF   1 meg

Since the coaxial cable which connects the probe to the scope has shunt capacitance, this capacitance must be added in parallel with the scope input capacitance as shown. If C_1 is properly adjusted so that the divider ratio V_v/V_p is constant, <u>sketch</u> the equivalent circuit seen at the probe input terminals (V_p). Assume $C_c = 53$ pf.

← (a)

For DC, the input signal is attenuated (reduced) by a factor of _____.

(b)

At all frequencies the input signal is attenuated by a factor of _____.

(c)

(a) scope ground   (b) +INPUT   (c) +INPUT and -INPUT
(d) circle EXT. TRIG.   (e) EXT. TRIG.   (f) EXT. INPUT

TURN TO FRAME 4.19

connected together (connected to the case and chassis)

1.21 | In this and the following frames, assume $S_v = S_h = 1$ volt/division. Also assume that the spot is centered when no inputs are applied.

A student has connected inputs
to the scope as shown.
The vertical deflection will be
_____ div.   (a)
The horizontal deflection will
be _____ div.   (b)

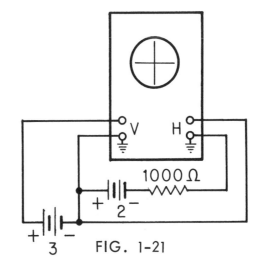

FIG. 1-21

(a) slope, (TRIGGER) SLOPE
(b) level, (TRIGGER) LEVEL

(c) the previous sweep waveform has gone
     to completion

2.21 | In the case illustrated below, the TRIGGER SLOPE control is set to + and the LEVEL control is set to 0. Sketch the trigger pulses and the resulting sweep waveform if the duration of the sweep is T_1 seconds.

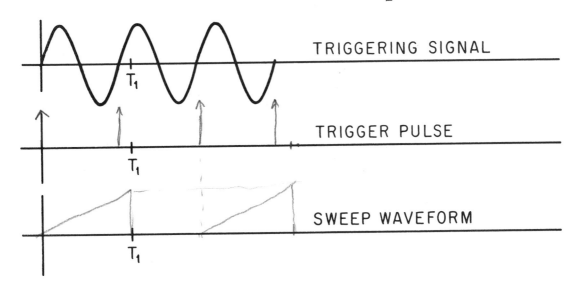

43

(a)

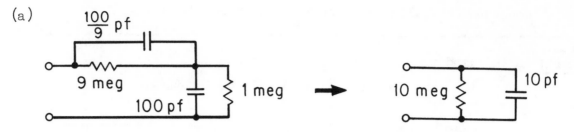

(b) V_v/V_p 1 meg/(9 meg + 1 meg) 1/10, so reduction is by a factor of 10

(c) 10 (since attenuation is independent of frequency)

3.21 The probe is used to measure the amplitude of a sine-wave source as shown below.

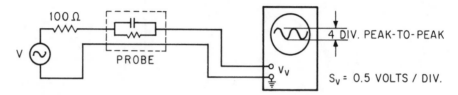

The peak-to-peak amplitude of V is _____ volts.

4.19 Indicate the proper connections to the scope for calibrating the time axis (step 1). Use 3 wires.　　　　　　　　　　　　　(a)

Trigger source should be set to _____.　　　(b)

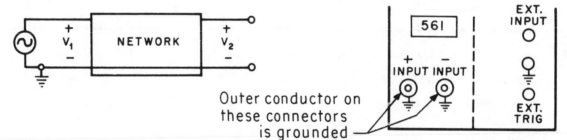

Note: The line drawn through the lower part of the network indicates that there is a common connection between v_1- and v_2-.

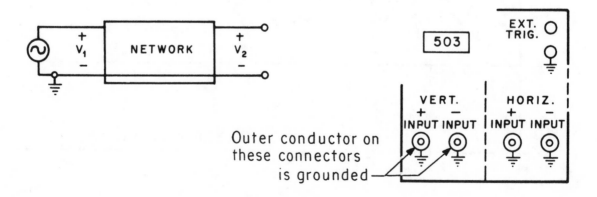

(a) 3 div

(b) If your answer is 1, 2, 3, -1, -2, or -3 continue with this frame
     (1.22). Otherwise, turn to frame 1.23.

1.22 Reexamine Fig. 1-21. The voltage which would be measured between the
two ground terminals is not 1, 2, 3, -1, -2, or -3 volts. What
would it be? _____   (a)

Note how the H input is connected. Now what is the horizontal deflection? _____   (b)

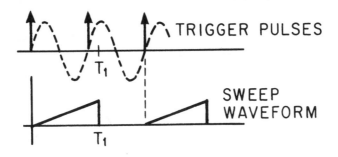

2.22 The waveform shown in Fig. 2-22a is used as the vertical input (v_v) and as
the triggering signal. If the control settings are TRIGGER LEVEL = 0,
TRIGGER SLOPE = +, sweep rate = .5 sec/div, sketch (on Fig. 2-22b) the
sweep waveform which is generated.

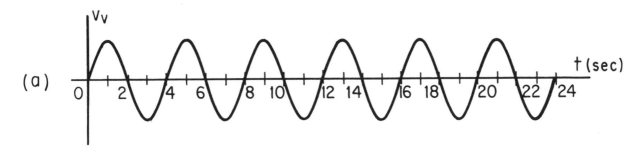

(a)

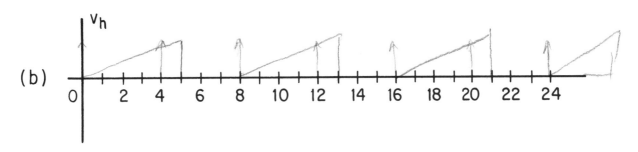

(b)

FIG. 2-22

20 volts (since V_v = 2 volts peak-to-peak and the probe attenuates the signal by a factor of 10).

3.22 When making accurate measurements with the scope, the probe should be used if the impedance of the source being measured is not small compared with the scope input impedance. In which of these cases should the probe be used?_____

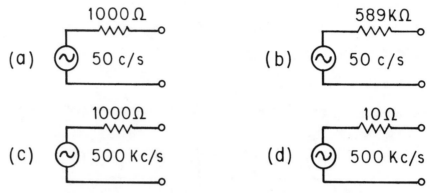

NOTE: input impedance of scope at 500 kc/s is approximately 6000 ohms.

(a) v_1+ to vertical +INPUT and to EXT. TRIG. input   (b) EXTernal
either v_1- or v_2- to scope ground

4.20 Indicate the proper connections to the scope for observing v_2 with the same time axis as v_1 (step 2). Use 3 wires.

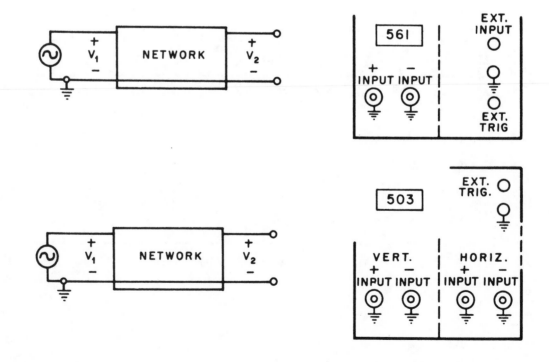

Answer to 1.21(b) and 1.22(b): The horizontal deflection is 0 (because the 2 volt source and series resistor is shorted out by the ground terminals).

This is a good place to take a break before you continue with the program.

Scope Traces Due to Time-Varying Inputs

1.23 Up to this point, we have learned how to determine the resulting deflection of the spot when constant voltages are applied to the input terminals. We are now going to investigate the patterns which are traced out on the scope screen when we apply time-varying voltages to the input terminals.

Unless specified otherwise, still assume that

$$S_v = S_h = 1 \text{ volt/div.}$$

Turn to the next frame.

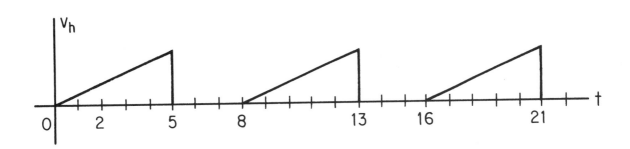

2.23 Now sketch the waveform which appears on the screen.

Assume that the spot starts at the left edge of the graticule when the sweep signal is 0, and assume that the peak value of the sweep voltage is sufficient to deflect the spot the full width of the screen.

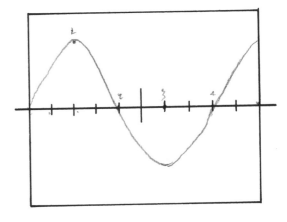

(b) and (c)

(Not (a) because 1000 << 1 megohm;

not (d) because 10 << 6000)

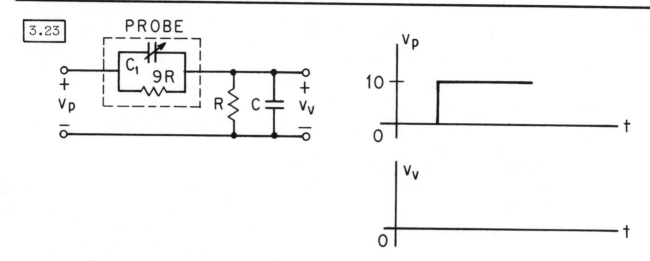

Assuming that the probe capacitance is properly adjusted, sketch v_v if v_p is as shown.

---

v_2+ to +INPUT (vert.), v_1+ to EXT. TRIG., either v_1- or v_2- to scope ground

---

4.21

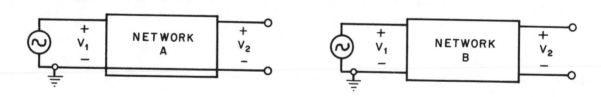

Network A has a common connection between v_1- and v_2-. Network B does <u>not</u> have a direct connection between v_1- and v_2-. In both cases, the scope ground is connected to the oscillator ground. When observing v_2 on the scope, <u>both</u> the +INPUT and -INPUT on the differential amplifier must be used for network _____ because _____

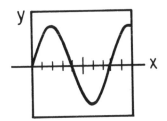

Note that 5 seconds of the waveform (1-1/4 cycles) appear on the scope screen.

2.24 In the preceding two frames, we had TRIGGER LEVEL = 0, TRIGGER SLOPE = +, and SWEEP RATE = 0.5 sec/div. The TRIGGER SLOPE is now changed to -. The vertical input and triggering signal are still the same.

Sketch the sweep waveform which is generated (on Fig. 2.24b).

Then sketch the waveform which appears on the screen (on Fig. 2.24c). Note that the trace always starts at the left edge of the screen no matter what time the sweep is triggered.

(a)

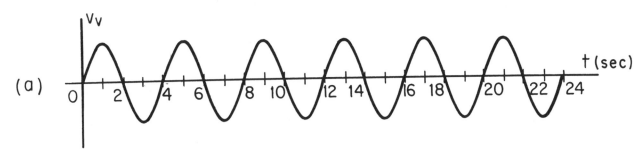

(b)

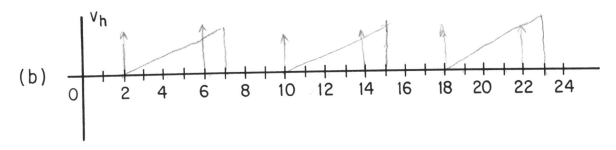

FIG. 2-24   (c)

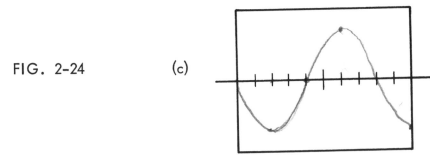

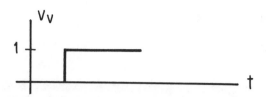

3.24 If the probe capacitance is not properly adjusted, the input voltage at the scope terminals will be distorted. In which of the following case(s) is the probe capacitance properly adjusted? _____

Probe
Input

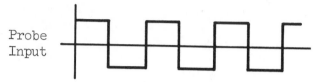

Waveforms displayed on screen:

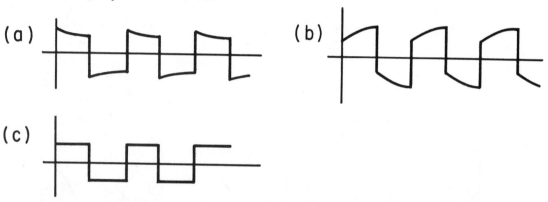

(a)

(b)

(c)

B because grounding v_2- would short out part of the network

4.22 In the network shown below, v_1 and v_2 do <u>not</u> have a common ground terminal, so v_1- and v_2- cannot be connected together. Indicate the proper connections to the scope for step (1) and step (2):

561
ONLY

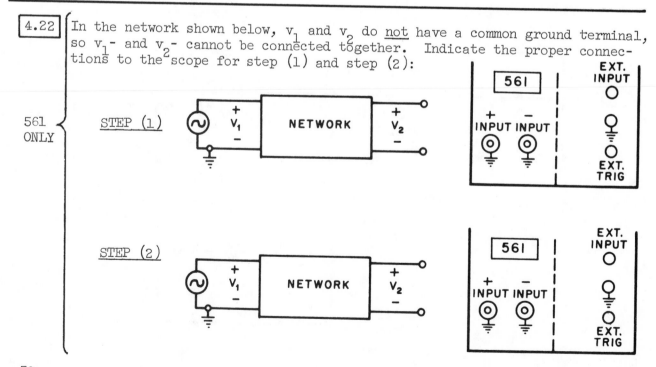

1.24 If the input voltage is time-varying, the spot will move across the screen. If $v_v = 0$ and v_h is as shown, indicate the position of the spot at t = 0, 1, 2, 3, and 4 on the grid. Label the points t = 0, t = 1, etc.

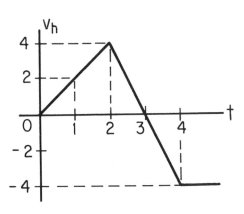 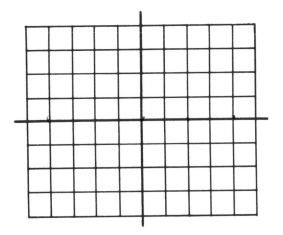

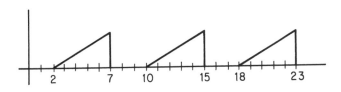 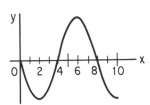

2.25 The waveform given below is used as a triggering signal. If the TRIGGER SLOPE is set to +, the sweep could trigger at points ____1____, ____2____, ____6____ depending on the setting of the level control.

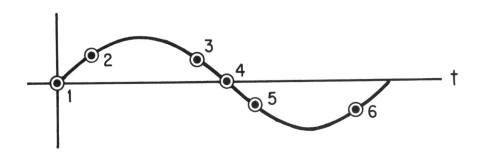

51

(c) only (in (a) and (b) the waveforms are distorted)

3.25 What is the effect of the probe on the scope input impedance?

_____ (a)

_____

When should the probe be used? _____ (b)

_____

The vertical sensitivity is set to S_v volts/div (without the probe).
When the probe is connected, if the vertical deflection is y divisions, the probe input voltage is _____. (c)
Given a square wave as a vertical input signal, how could you tell if
the probe capacitance was adjusted correctly? _____

_____ (d)

answers are on next page

4.23 In the network shown below, v_1 and v_2 do <u>not</u> have a common ground terminal,
so v_1- and v_2- cannot be connected together. Indicate the proper connections to the scope for step (1) and step (2):

503
ONLY

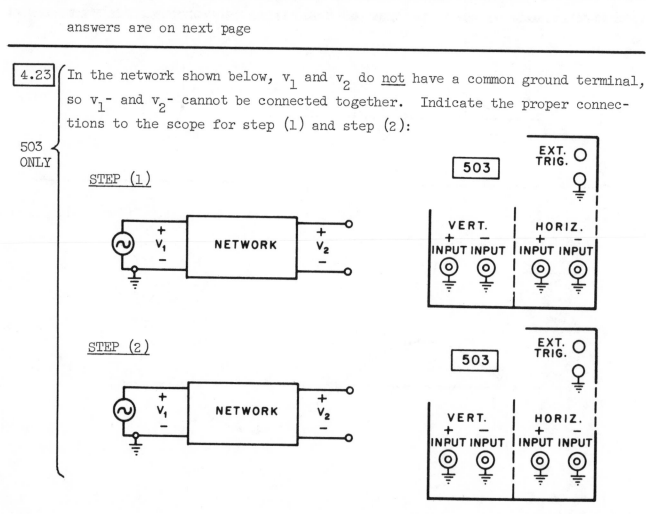

Plot on the x-axis as follows:

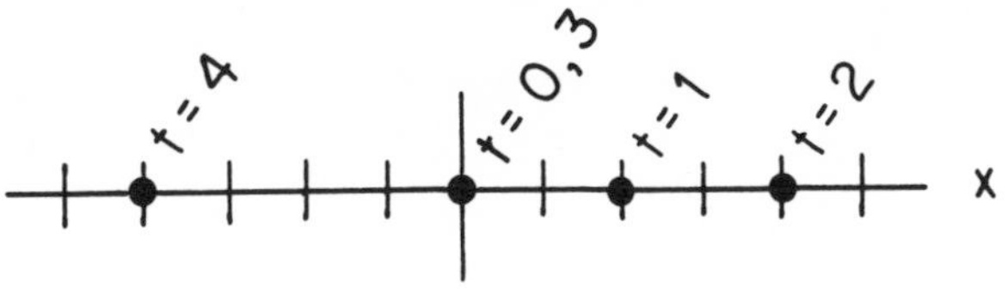

1.25 With $v_h = 0$ and $v_v = 2 \sin(2\pi \cdot 3t)$, the spot will move up and down

between the limits _____ divisions and (a)

_____ divisions at the rate of (b)

_____ cycles per second. (c)

---

1 2 6

2.26 In order to trigger at points 3, 4, or 5, the TRIGGER SLOPE must be

set to _____ neg _____. (a)

If the TRIGGER LEVEL control is set in the positive range, trigger-

ing will occur when the triggering signal is _____. (b)

To cause triggering to occur during the negative half cycle of the

triggering signal, the TRIGGER _____ (c)

should be set to _____. (d)

(a) the input impedance is increased by a factor of 10

(b) if the impedance of the circuit being measured is not small compared with the scope input impedance

(c) 10 S_y (the factor of 10 comes in because the probe divides the input voltage by 10)

(d) adjustment is correct if the waveform on the screen is an undistorted square wave

THIS IS A GOOD PLACE TO TAKE A BREAK

Other Measurement Errors

3.26 We have just studied how the probe can be used to reduce measurement errors which are due to loading. We will now consider several other sources of measurement errors.

There is a limit to how closely we can read the deflection from the screen, especially if we have to interpolate between divisions. It is usually difficult to read the deflection closer than the nearest 1/10 of a major division. Hence there may be a reading error of ± 1/20 division (or more if we aren't careful). Assuming a reading error of ± 1/20 division, what is the per cent reading error if the deflection is 4 divisions? _____ (a)

If the deflection is 1 division? _____ (b)

To minimize the per cent reading error, we should _____ (c)

_____ .

(a) v_1+ to +INPUT (vertical) and to EXT TRIG input

(b) v_2+ to +INPUT (vertical) and v_2- to -INPUT; v_1+ to EXT TRIG

oscillator ground to scope ground in both cases

TURN TO FRAME 4.24

54

(a) +2   (b) -2

(c) 3   (Remember that $f = \omega/2\pi$ where f is the frequency in cycles/sec;
ω is in radians/sec.)

1.26 If the frequency of the sine wave, $v_v = 2 \sin \omega t$,
is increased so that we cannot follow the motion
of the spot with our eye, sketch what we will see
on the grid below. (v_h still equals 0.)

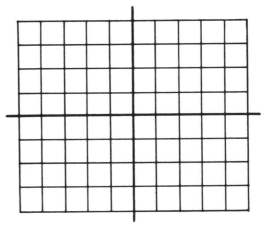

(a) - (minus)

(b) positive   (c) level   (d) (-) the negative range

2.27 For the given waveform, fill in the points at which the sweep will trigger
for the indicated control settings:

	LEVEL −	LEVEL 0	LEVEL +
SLOPE +	6	1	2
SLOPE −	5	4	3

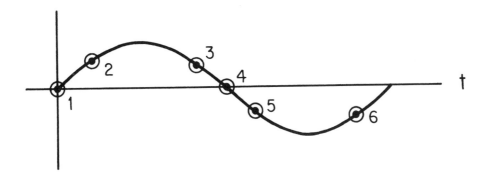

(a) $\dfrac{1/20}{4}$ x 100% = 1.25% (b) $\dfrac{1/20}{1}$ x 100% = 5%

(c) use as large a deflection as possible

3.27 With S_v = .2 volts/div, the following waveform is displayed on the screen.

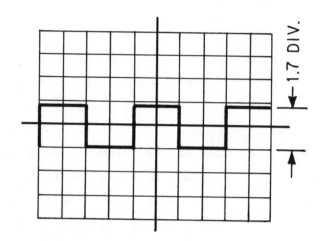

Assuming a reading error of ± 1/20 division, the peak-to-peak <u>voltage</u> is

_____ ± _____ %. (a)

To minimize per cent reading error, change S_v^* to _____ (b)

Sketch the resulting trace in the proper position on the screen. (c)

With this setting, the error is _____ % (d)

*Available values are 1, .5, .2, .05, .02, etc. volts/div.

4.24 The sweep is calibrated with v_1 = A sin ωt and the controls are adjusted to obtain Fig. 4-24x. Then v_2 = B sin(ωt + θ) is observed with the same time axis.

If $v_2(0) > 0$, then θ is a (+,-) _____ (a) angle between 0 and 180°.

If $v_2(0) < 0$, then θ is a _____ angle (b) between 0 and 180°.

For Fig. 4-24y give an equation for θ in terms of $θ_1$. θ = _____ (c)

For Fig. 4-24z give an equation for θ in terms of $θ_2$. θ = _____ (d)

Before you turn the page, check your an- to (c) and (d) by considering the limiting cases as $θ_1$ and $θ_2$ approach zero.

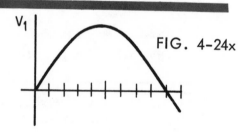

FIG. 4-24x

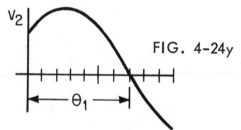

FIG. 4-24y

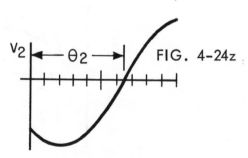

FIG. 4-24z

a vertical line on the y-axis between +2 and -2

1.27 With $v_v = 0$ and $v_h = 3 \sin \omega t$, the spot will move between the limits
_____ and _____ on the _____ axis.   (a b c)
Sketch the appearance of the scope trace at high frequencies on the
grid below.

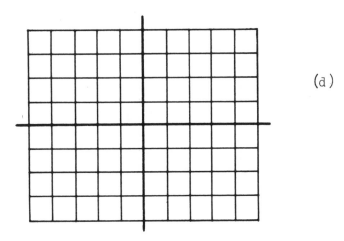

(d)

---

6 1 2   (Note that the functions of the SLOPE and LEVEL controls
5 4 3   are independent.)

2.28 The waveform of Fig. 2-27 is used as the vertical input and the controls
are set so triggering occurs at point 5.   TIME/DIV is set so that exactly
one cycle of the waveform appears on the screen.   Sketch the waveform as
it appears on the screen.

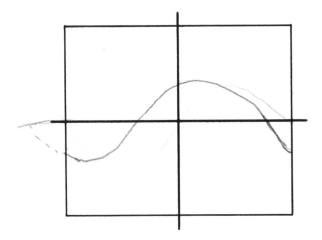

(a) .34 ± 2.9% (1.7 div x .2 volts/div = .34; $\frac{\pm.05\ div}{1.7\ div}$ x 100% = 2.9%)

(b) .05 volts/div

(c) square wave between +2.8 and -4 divisions (6.8 div. peak-to-peak)

(d) .74%

3.28

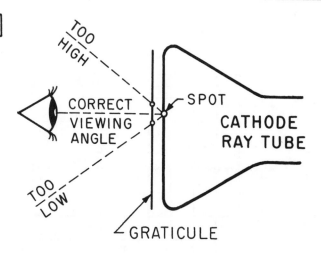

In many scopes, the graticule is a short distance in front of the screen. If the spot is viewed from too high or too low, it will appear in the wrong position with respect to the graticule lines as is shown in the diagram. This is known as parallax error. To avoid parallax error, one should view the scope

_____ (a)

_____

The 561A and 561B have internal graticules, which means the graticule lines are etched right on the surface of the screen. This completely eliminates _____ _____ (b)

(a) +   (b) -   (c) $\theta = 180 - \theta_1$ (d) $\theta = -\theta_2$

4.25 With the scope set as in frame 4.15 (20°/division), v_2 is observed for various values of θ. Give the value of θ in each case:

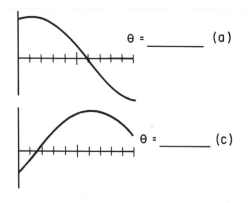

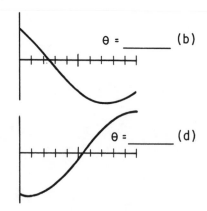

$\theta =$ _____ (a)

$\theta =$ _____ (b)

$\theta =$ _____ (c)

$\theta =$ _____ (d)

(a) +3   (b) -3   (c) x (horizontal)

(d) a horizontal line on the x-axis between +3 and -3

1.28 Plot the location of the spot when (1) $v_v = v_h = -2$, (2) $v_v = v_h = +1$,
(3) $v_v = v_h = +3$

If v_v and v_h are both functions of time with $v_v(t) = v_h(t)$, then at every
instant of time the spot will lie on a _____
through the origin at an angle of _____.

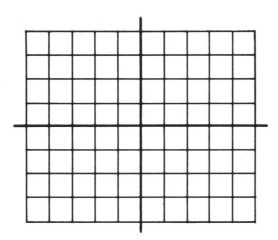

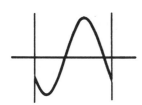

2.29 The level control is continuously variable from - through +. If the
level control is set more positive or more negative than the available triggering signal, the sweep will not be triggered. If the
level is set in the + range and no triggering is observed, either the
trigger level should be (increased/decreased) ___*decreased*___ (a)
or the input signal should be ___*increased*___ in magnitude. (b)

(a) directly in front of the screen

(b) parallax error

3.29 In addition to the errors in reading the scope, there are errors which are inherent in the scope itself. Even if the scope is properly calibrated, there may be a calibration error of as much as ± 3%.* For example if VOLTS/DIV is set to 1, the actual volts/division may be anywhere between .97 and 1.03.

Assuming a calibration error of ± 3% in addition to a reading error of ± 1/20 division, if S_v = .5 volt/div and the deflection is 5 divisions, the input voltage has a nominal value of _____, (a) but it may actually lie anywhere in the range _____ to

_____. (b)

*1.5% for 561B

(a) 60°   (b) 130°   (c) -30°   (d) -110°

4.26 Given v_1 = A sin ωt, v_2 = B sin(ωt + θ), -90°<θ<0°

Explain (a) how you would calibrate the scope so that each division represents 10° and (b) how you would determine θ. State where v_1 and v_2 should be connected and sketch the expected waveforms for θ = -45°.

(a)

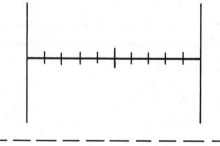

(b)

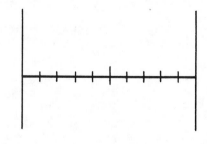

(a) line   (b) 45°

1.29 Sketch the appearance of the trace when

$$v_v(t) = v_h(t) = 4 \cos \omega t$$

Hint: Plot limiting values first.

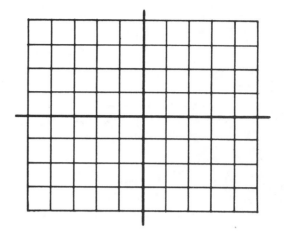

(a) decreased   (b) increased

THIS IS A GOOD PLACE TO TAKE A BREAK

Trigger Source

2.30 As shown in Fig. 5-3 (p. 211), the triggering signal may come from 3 different sources. If you want the triggering signal to have the same waveshape as the vertical input, the TRIGGER SOURCE switch should be set to _____Internal_____. If you want to trigger the   (a)
sweep from a different source than the vertical input or the AC line, the TRIGGER SOURCE should be set to _____External_____.   (b)

(a) 2.5 volts   (b) 2.4 to 2.6 $(2.5 \pm 3\% \pm 1\%)$

3.30 Errors may occur if we try to use the scope with input signals which have too high a frequency.

Suppose that we use the scope to observe a cosine wave, A cos $(2\pi ft)$. The vertical sensitivity is set at some convenient value, say 1 volt/div. We will hold the amplitude of the input sine wave constant and vary the frequency. If the scope were an ideal measuring instrument, the peak vertical deflection should (increase, decrease, remain constant) _____ as f is increased.   (a)

Since the scope is not ideal, the peak deflection may vary as f is varied even if the peak input voltage is constant. The peak response of a scope to the input A cos $(2\pi ft)$ is plotted below. If we want to use this scope to make <u>accurate</u> voltage measurements, the maximum frequency which can be used is approximately _____.   (b)

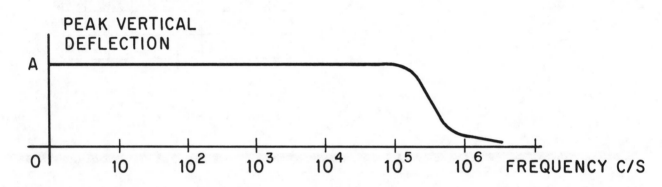

(a) Connect v_1 to both the vertical input and the ext. trigger input.
With the scope set on external trigger, adjust for the picture at the
left.

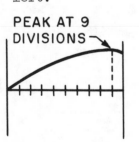

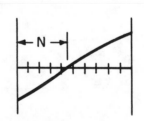

(b) Then change the vertical
input to v_2. Read the
number of divisions as
indicated.

$\theta = -(N \text{ div.} \times 10°/\text{div.})$

TURN TO FRAME 4.27 ON PAGE 66

limiting values: when cos ωt = -1, x = y = -4
                   when cos ωt = +1, x = y = +4

so draw a diagonal line from (x = y = -4) to (x = y = +4)

1.30 If $v_v = Kv_h$, the spot will lie on a(an) _____ whose   (a)

equation is   y = _____.   (b)

Sketch the trace if $v_v = 2 \sin \omega t$, $v_h = -4 \sin \omega t$.

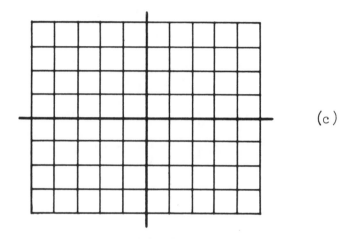

(c)

(a) INTernal   (b) EXTernal

2.31 When the SOURCE is set to LINE, the triggering signal is the 60 c/s AC line.

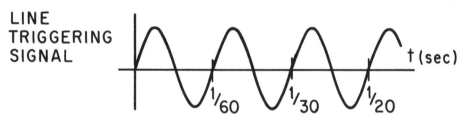

LINE TRIGGERING SIGNAL

If the sweep duration, T, is less than 1/60 sec, the sweep will be

triggered _____60_____ times per second. If 1/60 < T < 1/30, the   (a)

sweep will be triggered _____30_____ times per second. The sweep   (b)

will be triggered 20 times per second, if T lies in the range

_____$1/30$_____ < T < _____$1/20$_____.   (c)

3.31   The response of the scope at low frequencies depends on whether the
input switch is set to AC or DC. Figs. 3.31a and 3.31b show the
response curves of the same scope for two different settings of the
input switch.   Label the curves with the appropriate switch setting.   (a)

If AC input is selected, the frequency range in which accurate voltage measurements can be made is about _____ to
_____.   (b)

If we want to measure the peak value of a 5 c/s sine wave
_____ input should be used.   (c)

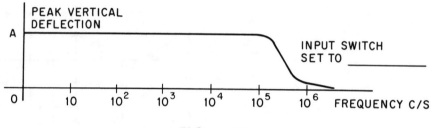

FIG. 3-31a

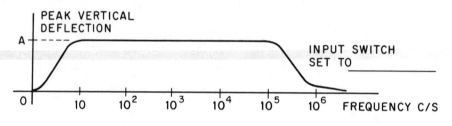

FIG. 3-31b

TURN TO FRAME 4.27

(a) line   (b) y = Kx

(c) a diagonal line between $(x = -4, y = +2)$ and $(x = +4, y = -2)$

1.31 If $v_h = 4 \cos \omega t$ and $v_v = 4 \sin \omega t$, plot the location of the spot for
$\omega t = 0, \pi/4, \pi/2, 3\pi/4, \ldots, 2\pi$. As the spot moves, it traces out
a(an) _____. Put an arrow on the plot which indicates the
direction of motion of the spot.

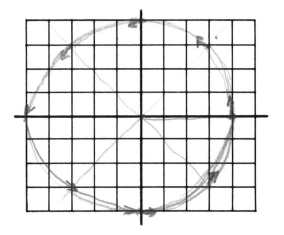

(a) 60   (b) 30   (c) $1/30 < T < 1/20$

2.32 If the sweep waveform and vertical input are as shown below, would a
stable picture be obtained on the screen? ____no____.

Explain __no repeating same waveform at same point__
__sweep starts at different points__

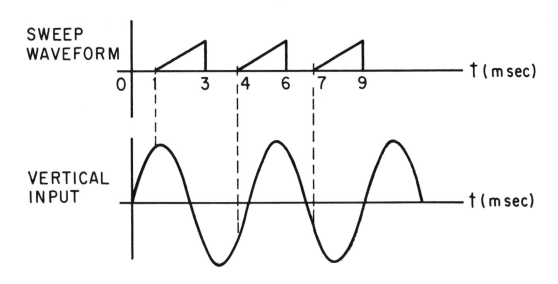

SWEEP
WAVEFORM

VERTICAL
INPUT

(a) 3-31a is DC input and 3-31b is AC input

(b) 10 c/s to 10^5 c/s   (c) DC

3.32 We have studied several types of errors which can reduce the accuracy of measurements made with the scope. For each type of error, state what can be done to reduce the effects of the error.

Loading error._____ (a)

_____

Parallax error._____ (b)

_____

Reading error._____ (c)

_____

The calibration error which is inherent in the scope may be as large

as _____.   (d)

Errors may also occur if the frequency of the input signal is

_____.   (e)

4.27 In the given network, v_1 and v_2 do <u>not</u> have a common ground terminal. The phase angle of v_2 with respect to v_1 is to be measured by the triggered sweep method. Indicate the proper connections to the scope. (Assume that the time axis has already been calibrated.)

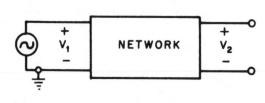

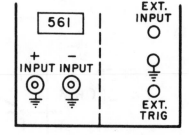

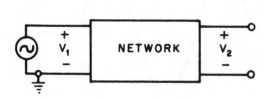

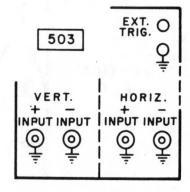

circle (of radius 4)
spot moves counterclockwise

1.32 In the preceding frame, the vertical deflection is $y = 4 \sin \omega t$ and the horizontal deflection is $x = 4 \cos \omega t$. Verify analytically that the trace is a circle by eliminating the parameter ωt from the equations.

(a)

Hint: $\sin^2 \omega t + \cos^2 \omega t = 1$

Will there be any change in the appearance of the trace if the x and y inputs are interchanged? _____ (b)

NO. The sweep starts at a different point in each cycle.

2.33 The vertical input and the sweep are said to be synchronized if the sweep is triggered at the same point in every cycle of the vertical input.

When the vertical input is a periodic waveform, what relation must exist between the vertical input and the sweep in order to obtain a stable trace on the screen? ___triggered at same point___ (a)
must both synchronized
The proper relation will be obtained if the TRIGGER SOURCE is set to

___internal___. (b)

(a) use the probe   (b) view scope directly in front of screen

(c) use as large a deflection as possible (turn up the gain)

(d) 3%   (e) too high (or too low if the AC input is used)

THIS IS A GOOD PLACE TO TAKE A BREAK

Use of the Differential Amplifier

3.33 So far you have used only the +INPUT of the differential amplifier in lab. The differential mode of operation has not been used. This section discusses use of the differential amplifier in the differential mode.

The voltage applied between the +INPUT and ground will be called v_+ and the voltage applied between the -INPUT and ground will be called v_-.

A network is connected to the vertical amplifier as shown. For this connection, v_+ = _____ and v_- = _____.

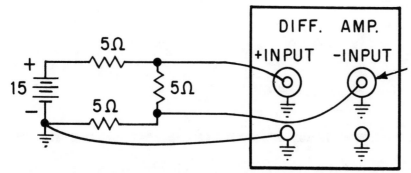

Note: outer conductor is ground; inner conductor is -INPUT

Connect + side of v_1 to EXT. TRIG. and - side to ground.
Connect + side of v_2 to +INPUT and - side to -INPUT (on vertical amplifier).
(The differential amplifier must be used in the differential mode since there is no common ground between v_1 and v_2.

THIS IS A GOOD PLACE TO TAKE A BREAK

Phase Shift Measurement by the Ellipse Method

4.28 We will now discuss the ellipse method for phase shift measurement with the scope. As in the triggered sweep method just discussed, the object of the method is to determine the phase angle between sinusoidal voltages, v_1 and v_2. Instead of displaying v_1 and v_2 as functions of time, we will display v_2 vs v_1.

    561: How should the TIME/DIV switch be set (see Fig. 5-1, p. 207)?
    _____

    503: How should the Horizontal Display switch be set (see Fig. 5-2, p. 208)? _____

(a) Squaring and adding the two equations gives $x^2 + y^2 = 4^2$ which is the equation of a circle of radius 4.

(b) No. (since $y^2 + x^2 = 4^2$ is still a circle of radius 4)

1.33 If $v_h = A \sin \omega t$, in order to obtain a circular trace, v_v must be

_____, but the trace will be a diagonal line (a)

(not necessarily at 45°) if v_v = _____. (b)

If $v_h = B \cos \omega t$, in order to obtain a circular trace, v_v must be

_____, but the trace will be a diagonal line (not (c)

necessarily at 45°) if v_v = _____. (d)

(a) vertical input and sweep must be <u>synchronized</u>   (b) INTernal

---

2.34 A voltage v_x is applied to the external trigger input and v_v is applied to the vertical input. The trigger SOURCE is set to EXT, the SLOPE is set to +, and the LEVEL is set to trigger when v_x is -1 volt. Draw an arrow to indicate the point on v_x at which triggering occurs. Draw an arrow on v_v to indicate the time at which the sweep begins. Then sketch v_v as it will appear on the screen if the sweep rate is 1 ms/div.

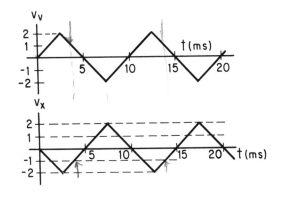
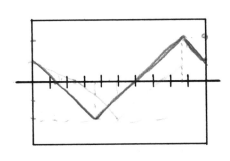

(a) + 10 volts   (b) +5 volts (note that the 15 volt source divides
                              equally across the 3 resistors)

3.34 When both inputs to the differential amplifier are used, the vertical
deflection is

$$y = (v_+ - v_-) / S_v$$

If $v_+ = 10$, $v_- = -5$, and $S_v = 5$ volts/div, the vertical deflection
is _____   (a)

If v_+ and v_- are as shown, sketch the trace if $S_v = 2$ volts/div.
(Assume + TRIGGER SLOPE AND 0 TRIGGER LEVEL.)

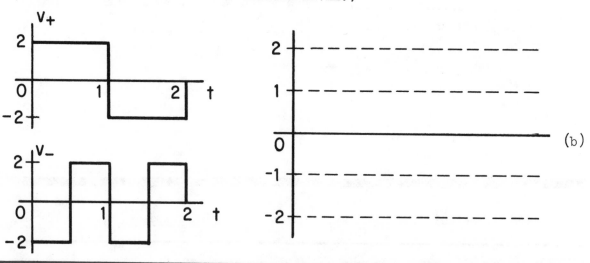

(b)

561:   to EXT. INPUT   503:   to HORIZ. AMPLIFIER (SWEEP DISABLED)

4.29 Indicate the connections to the scope required to display v_2 (on the vertical vs v_1 (on the horizontal) for the network shown below:

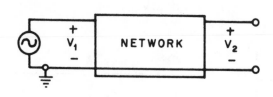

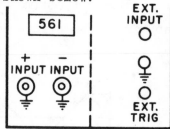

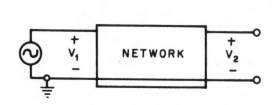

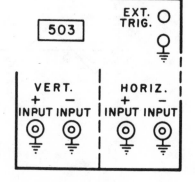

70

(a) A cos ωt   (b) A_1 sin ωt (A_1 does not have to equal A)

(c) B sin ωt   (d) B_1 cos ωt (B_1 does not have to equal B)

1.34 If the amplitude of the vertical signal used to obtain the circular trace in frame 1.31 is reduced and the horizontal signal remains the same, sketch the appearance of the modified trace.

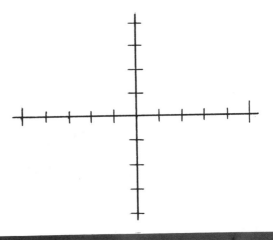

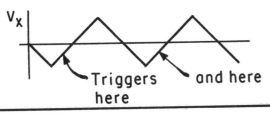

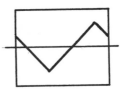

Triggers here   and here

2.35

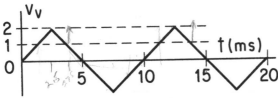

v_v is the vertical input
v_x is the external trigger input
TRIGGER SLOPE set to - (negative)
TRIGGER LEVEL set to trigger
  when the triggering signal
  v_v or v_x is +1 volt
sweep rate = 1 ms/div
Sketch the trace if
(a) TRIGGER SOURCE set to
     INTernal
(b) TRIGGER SOURCE set to
     EXTernal

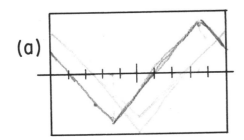

(a)

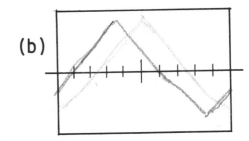

(b)

71

(a) $\dfrac{10 - (-5)}{5} = 3$

(b)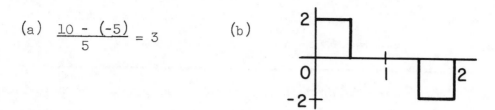

3.35 It is desired to observe v_a with the scope. Terminal 2 cannot be connected to the scope ground because _____ (a)

The voltage from terminal 1 to ground is $v_a + v_b$; the voltage from terminal 2 to ground is v_b. Indicate how to connect the scope so that $v_+ - v_- = v_a$ (b)

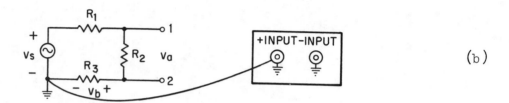

With the above connections, if the sensitivity is S_v, the vertical deflection is y = _____ (c)

If you have a connection to EXT. TRIG. turn back and try again.

Check your answer for the following connections:

    ground side of v_1 and/or v_2 connected to scope ground

    ungrounded side of v_2 connected to center conductor of +INPUT (vertical)

    ungrounded side of v_1 connected to EXT. INPUT (561) or horizontal
      +INPUT (503)

4.30 Assume that $S_v = S_h = 1$ volt/div. If the horizontal input is $v_1 = A \sin \omega t$ and the vertical input is $v_2 = A \sin (\omega t + 30°)$ plot the resulting trace on the opposite graph. (Plot the spot location for $\omega t = 0$, 30, 60, 90, 120, 150, and 180 degrees and complete the figure by symmetry.)

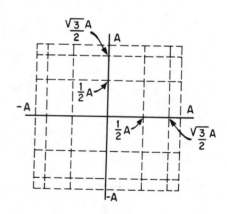

an ellipse

1.35 As we have seen, a circular or elliptical trace can be obtained by using a cosine wave and a sine wave as H and V inputs to the scope. The circuit of Fig. 1-35 will be used in lab to produce the required H and V signals.

If we assume that the magnitude of the impedance of the capacitor, $1/\omega C$, is much less than R, the voltage _____ is negligible (a) compared with the voltage v_2, and

$v_2 \approx$ _____. (b)

$i = v_2/R \approx$ _____ (c)

= _____ $\cos \omega t$ (d)

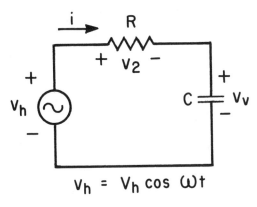

$v_h = V_h \cos \omega t$

FIG. 1-35

The voltage across C is then

$v_v = \frac{1}{C} \int i \, dt \approx$ _____ $\sin \omega t$ (e)

(substitute for i and carry out the integration)

This approximation is valid if

$1/\omega C \ll R$ or ωRC _____ 1 (f)

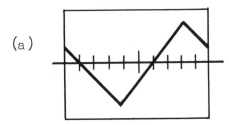

(a)   (b)

(triggers when $v_v = 1$ with neg. slope)   (triggers when $v_x = 1$ with neg. slope)

2.36 If the frequency of the vertical input is 70 c/s, could a stable picture be obtained if the TRIGGER SOURCE is LINE?___No_____ (a)

Explain ___70 c/s > 60 c/s → not synchronized___

With the same vertical input, if the frequency of the trigger input is 35 c/s, could a stable picture be obtained if the TRIGGER SOURCE is EXTernal?__yes_____ Explain ___multiple of 70 c/s___ (b)

___so synchronized___

(a) R_3 would be shorted out (v_a would change)

(b) terminal 1 to +INPUT, terminal 2 to -INPUT (center terminals)

(c) $y = v_a/S_v$

3.36 Follow these rules when connecting a circuit to the scope:

Rule 1. If some point in the circuit is grounded, connect the circuit ground to the scope ground. Do not rely on the line cord grounds for a connection.

Rule 2. If a voltage to be connected to the scope has one side grounded, then use only the +INPUT on the differential amplifier. (Ground the -INPUT with a switch.)

Rule 3. If a voltage to be connected to the scope has neither side in common with the circuit ground, use both the +INPUT and -INPUT on the differential amplifier.

Indicate proper connections to the scope to observe v_1 for each of the following circuits:

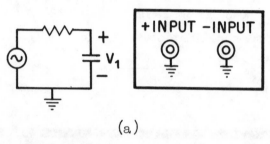

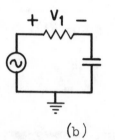

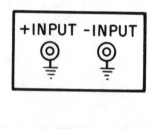

(a)   (b)

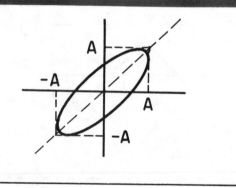

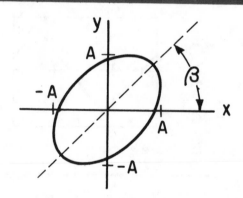

4.31 The angle between the major axis of the ellipse which you just plotted and the x-axis is _____ degrees.   (a)

Let $x = A \sin \omega t$ and $y = A \sin(\omega t + \theta)$. The figure at the right gives a plot of y vs x for $\theta = 60°$. Sketch the trace for $\theta = 0$ and $\theta = 90°$ on the same figure. Describe how the x-y plot changes as θ (b)
is varied from 0 to 90°.

_____   (c)

As θ increases, the angle β between the axis of the ellipse and the x-axis (increases/remains the same/decreases)

_____   (d)

(a) v_v (b) v_h (c) v_h/R (d) V_h/R (e) $V_h/\omega RC$ (f) $\gg$

1.36 As we have just shown, the output of the network of Fig. 1-35 is

$$v_v = (V_h/\omega RC) \sin \omega t$$

A student connects the network of Fig. 1-35 to the scope as shown be-
low, with $v_h = 4 \cos \omega t$ $(V_h = 4)$ and $\omega RC = 10$. The scope settings
are $S_v = S_h = 1$ volt/div. He observes an ellipse on the screen. In
order to obtain a circular trace of radius 4 divisions, which of the
scope settings should be changed? _____   (a)

To what value? _____   (b)

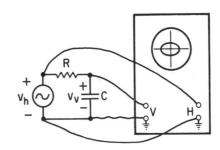

(a) No. The line frequency is 60 c/s so the sweep would not be synchronized with the vertical input.

(b) Yes. 35 c/s is exactly half of 70 c/s.

2.37 The sweep will <u>not</u> trigger at a point of zero slope on the triggering
signal. Suppose that v_1
and v_2 are available as
inputs and we wish to
display the following on
the screen:

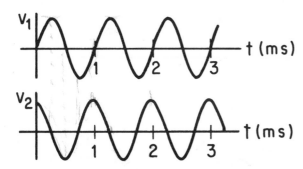

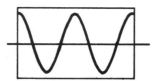

v_1 should be connected to the ___VERTICAL EXTERNAL TRIG___   (a)

v_2 should be connected to the ___EXT TRIG VERTICAL___   (b)

The controls should be set as follows:

TRIGGER SOURCE ___EXTERNAL TRIG___ SLOPE ___↗___ LEVEL ___0___   (c,d,e)

TIME/DIV ___.2 ms/div___   (f)

(a) circuit ground to scope ground; + side of v_1 to +INPUT

(b) circuit ground to scope ground; + side of v_1 to +INPUT;
     - side of v_1 to -INPUT

3.37 Given two signals, v_+ and v_-, the difference component is defined as

$$\Delta v = v_+ - v_-$$

The component which is common to both signals, or common-mode component, is

$$v_c = \frac{1}{2} \left(v_+ + v_- \right)$$

For each of the following pairs of signals, find the difference component and the common-mode component:

v_+	v_-	difference component	common-mode component	
5	1	_____	_____	(a)
$2 + 3 \sin \omega t$	$-2 + 3 \sin \omega t$	_____	_____	(b)
$2 \cos \omega t$	$4t$	_____	_____	(c)

(a) 45   (b) 45° diagonal line and circle of radius A

(c) the plot changes from a straight line to an ellipse to a circle (the ellipse grows fatter as θ increases)

(d) remains the same (The major axis is always at a 45° angle with the x-axis when $0<\theta<90°$ if the maximum values of x and y are the same.)

4.32 The observed trace for $x = A \sin \omega t$ and $y = B \sin(\omega t + \theta)$ is given below for two different values of A. The angle β between the major axis of the ellipse and the x-axis depends only on (check one):

the value of θ _____   the relative values of A and B _____   (a)

The angle β is 45° only if _____.   (b)

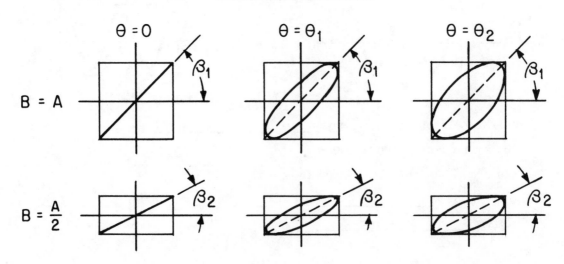

(a) S_V (vertical)   (b) 0.1 volt/div (since $v_v = .4 \sin \omega t$ and we want
a maximum deflection of 4 divisions)

THIS IS A GOOD PLACE TO TAKE A BREAK

Signals with AC and DC Components

1.37 You have now learned the relation between the voltages applied to the input
terminals of the scope and the resulting deflection of the spot on the
screen. In some cases the input voltage to the scope will have both AC and
DC components. In the next sequence of frames, you will learn how to set
the scope so that it will respond only to the AC component instead of to
the entire input voltage.

By the DC component of a periodic voltage waveform we mean its average
value. The average can be taken over one period. Give the DC component of
each waveform in Fig. 1-37.

(a) _____   (b) _____   (c) _____

(d) _____

Hint: Parts (a), (b) and (c) can be done by inspection. Use integration
for part (d).

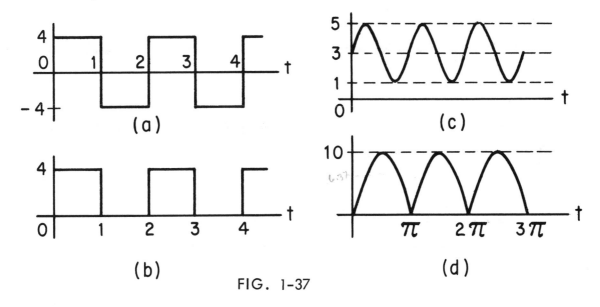

FIG. 1-37

TURN TO FRAME 2.38

(a) 4   3   (b) 4   3 sin ωt
(c) 2 cos ωt - 4t   cos ωt + 2t

3.38 If the inputs to the differential amplifier are v_+ and v_-, the difference component of the input voltage is $\Delta v =$ _____ and the   (a)
common-mode component is $v_c =$ _____   (b)

An <u>ideal</u> differential amplifier amplifies the difference component and
rejects the common-mode component. If the vertical sensitivity is S_v,
the vertical deflection produced by an <u>ideal</u> differential amplifier

is $y =$ _____   (c)

The difference mode gain is defined as $K_d = 1/S_v$. For the ideal differential amplifier, express y in terms of the difference mode gain.

      $y =$ _____   (d)

(a) the relative values of A and B   (b) A = B

4.33 $x = A \sin \omega t$ $y = A \sin(\omega t + \theta)$

If $\theta = 180°$, the relation between x and y is y = _____.

Sketch the x-y plot for $\theta = 180°$.

What do you think the plot will look
like if θ is between 90° and 180°?
Sketch your answer for θ about 135°.

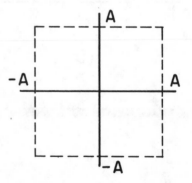

(a) 0   (b) 2   (c) 3   (d) $\frac{1}{\pi} \int_0^\pi 10 \sin t \, dt = \frac{20}{\pi} = 6.37$

1.38 To obtain the AC component of a periodic voltage waveform, subtract the DC component from the total voltage.

Sketch the AC component of each of the waveforms shown in Fig. 1-37. Specify the peak values of the AC component.

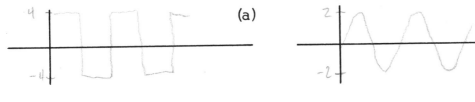

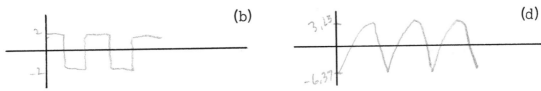

Note that for the AC component, the area below the axis is equal to the area above the axis, so the average value of the AC component is always _____.

(e)

Two different solutions are possible:

(a) vertical input   (b) ext. trigger input   (c) EXT.   (d) -
(e) 0   (f) .2 ms/div.
OR
(a) ext. trigger input (b) vertical input   (c) EXT. (d) +
(e) 0   (f) .2 ms/div

2.38 When observing a periodic signal with the scope, the proper TRIGGER SOURCE must be selected in order to obtain a stable picture. Complete the following table giving all allowable settings of the TRIGGER SOURCE switch which would give a stable trace:

Vertical Input	External Trigger Input	Allowable Settings of Trigger Source	
120 c/s	NONE	INTERNAL, LINE	(a)
56 c/s	28 c/s	EXTERNAL, INT.	(b)
140 c/s	60 c/s	INT, EXT	(c)
1190 c/s	DC	INT	(d)

79

(a) $v_+ - v_-$ (b) $\frac{1}{2}(v_+ + v_-)$ (c) $\frac{1}{S_v}(v_+ - v_-)$

(d) $K_d(v_+ - v_-)$

3.39 Several difficulties may be encountered in the differential mode of operation because the differential amplifier is not ideal. Instead of producing a vertical deflection of

$$y = K_d(v_+ - v_-)$$

the actual deflection is

$$y = K_d(v_+ - v_-) + K_c \frac{v_+ + v_-}{2} = K_d\Delta v + K_c v_c$$

K_d is called the _____ gain and   (a)

K_c is called the common-mode gain.

If $y = 10\Delta v + .1 v_c$, the common-mode gain is _____ and the   (b)

difference mode gain is _____.   (c)

For an ideal differential amplifier, K_c = _____   (d)

(a) $y = -x$

(b,c)

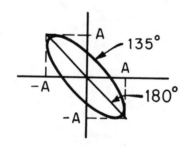

4.34 Sketch the location of the major axis of the ellipse

    (a) if $0 \leq \theta < 90°$

    (b) if $90° < \theta \leq 180°$

If the ellipse is very thin, θ is close to _____ or _____   (c)

If the ellipse is very fat, θ is close to _____.   (d)

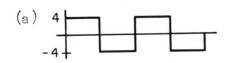

(a) 4 / -4

(b) 2 / -2

(c) 2 / -2

(d) 3.63 / -6.37

(e) 0

$\boxed{1.39}$ State the relation between a voltage $v(t)$, its DC component V_{DC}, and its AC component $v_{AC}(t)$.

$$v(t) = V_{DC} + V_{AC}(t)$$

(a) INT, LINE   (b) INT, EXT   (c) INT   (d) INT

THIS IS A GOOD PLACE TO TAKE A BREAK

Trigger Coupling

$\boxed{2.39}$ The coupling circuit for the input to the triggering circuit is shown below. The triggering signal is direct coupled to the input of the trigger pulse generator when the COUPLING switch is set to ___DC___. (a)
The signal is coupled through a blocking capacitor when the switch is set to ___AC___. The DC level of the triggering signal does not (b)
affect the sweep circuit when the coupling is set to ___AC___. (c)

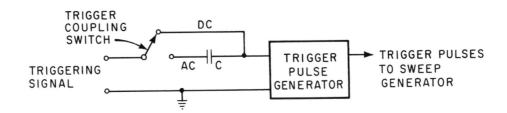

(a) difference mode   (b) .1   (c) 10   (d) 0

3.40 The vertical deflection produced by a non-ideal differential amplifier

is   y = _____   (a)

(Express your answer in terms of K_d, K_c, v_+ and v_-)

The <u>common-mode rejection ratio</u>* (CMRR) is defined as the ratio of
the difference mode gain to the common mode gain:

$$CMRR = K_d/K_c$$

If y = 15 Δv + .2 v_c, the common-mode rejection ratio is _____   (b)

If the differential amplifier is ideal, the common-mode gain is _____, (c)

so the common-mode rejection ratio is _____.   (d)

A good differential amplifier will have a (high/low) _____ CMRR.   (e)

_____

* also called differential rejection ratio

(a)

(b)

(c) 0° or 180°

(d) 90°

4.35 If we change the sign of θ from + to -, the x-y plot will be unchanged.
(Proof of this statement is given in the next frame.)

Is it possible to distinguish between θ = 60° and θ = -60° using the
ellipse method? _____   (a)

Between θ = 30° and θ = 330°? _____   (b)

A student determines that θ = -120° (or 240°) by the ellipse method.
What other value might θ have? _____   (c)

What method of phase measurement could be used to determine which of
the two values is correct?

_____   (d)

$$v(t) = V_{DC} + v_{AC}(t)$$

1.40 In Fig. 1-40a, the steady-state DC current flowing through C and R is

i = _____0_____ and the steady-state DC voltage across R is (a)

v_R = _____0_____. The steady-state DC voltage across the capaci- (b)

tor is v_C = ____V_{DC}____. (c)

In Fig. 1-40b, assume that the impedance of the capacitor is very

small compared with R at all frequencies present in $v_{AC}(t)$. The

voltage across the resistor is v_R = ____v_{AC}____. (d)

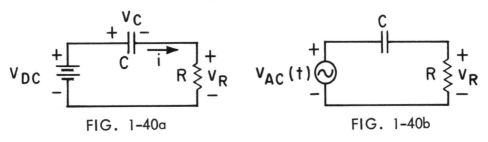

FIG. 1-40a   FIG. 1-40b

In this example, the capacitor acts like a(an) ___STORAGE OPEN___ (e)

circuit for DC and a(an)____SHORT____ circuit for AC. (f)

(a) DC   (b) AC   (c) AC

2.40

561 ONLY

The trigger circuit has two types of AC coupling--AC SLOW and AC FAST. AC SLOW and AC FAST coupling differ only in the size of the blocking capacitor. AC FAST is used only for special applications, so it will not be discussed further. When AC coupling is required, always use <u>AC SLOW</u>. In the rest of this program, we will consider only DC and AC SLOW coupling.

If we want the triggering circuit to respond to the entire input wave-

form including any DC component, the trigger coupling should be set

to ____DC____ (a)

If we want the triggering circuit to respond to only the time-varying

component of the input, we should set the trigger coupling to

____AC SLOW____. (b)

(a) $K_d(v_+ - v_-) + K_c \dfrac{v_+ + v_-}{2}$ (b) $15/.2 = 75$

(c) 0   (d) infinity   (e) high

3.41   In order to measure the CMMR, we must determine K_d and K_c. Given that $y = K_d(v_+ - v_-) + K_c \dfrac{v_+ + v_-}{2}$ what is the deflection if

$v_+ = v_- = v_1$? $y =$ _____   (a)

Indicate how we should connect an oscillator to determine K_c.

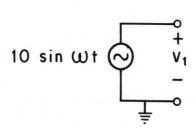 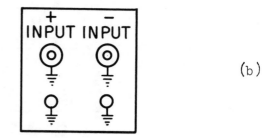   (b)

With this connection, if the peak vertical deflection is 1 division

$K_c =$ _____ div/volt   (c)

(a) NO (since changing the sign of θ does not change the x-y plot)

(b) NO (330° is the same as -30°)

(c) 120° (or -240°)

(d) triggered sweep method

4.36   Proof follows that changing the sign of the phase angle does not change the ellipse which is displayed. (You may skip the rest of this frame if you wish.)

Assume that the horizontal deflection is $x = A \sin \omega t$ and the vertical deflection is $y = B \sin(\omega t + \theta)$. At time t_1, the spot is located at $x_1 = A \sin \omega t_1$, $y = B \sin(\omega t_1 + \theta)$. If we change the y deflection to

$$y = B \sin(\omega t - \theta), \text{ at time } t_2 = (\pi/\omega) - t_1 \text{ we have}$$

$$x = A \sin \omega t_2 = A \sin(\pi - \omega t_1) = A \sin \omega t_1 = x_1$$

$$\text{and } y = B \sin(\omega t_2 - \theta) = B \sin(\pi - \omega t_1 - \theta) = B \sin(\omega t_1 + \theta) = y_1$$

Hence for every point (x_1, y_1) on the original ellipse, there is a corresponding point on the ellipse which is obtained when the sign of θ is changed. In one complete cycle, the same set of points is traced out in both cases, so the resulting ellipses are identical.

84

(a) i = 0 (since DC current cannot flow through a capacitor)

(b) $v_R = iR = 0$.(c) $v_C = V_{DC}$ (since there is no voltage across R)

(d) $v_R = v_{AC}(t)$ (since the voltage drop across C is negligible)

(e) open (for DC)   (f) short (for AC)

1.41 In the circuit below, what is the DC component of $v_1(t)$? _____0_____ (a)

If the impedance of the capacitor is very small compared with R at all

frequencies present in $v_{AC}(t)$, $v_1(t) = $ ____$v_{AC}(t)/R$____ (b)

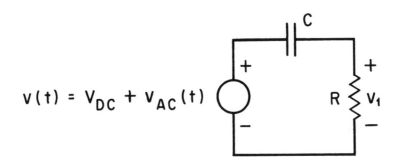

$$v(t) = V_{DC} + v_{AC}(t)$$

(a) DC   (b) AC (AC SLOW for 561)

2.41 When observing very low frequency signals, the AC-DC-GND switch on

the vertical amplifier should be set to _____DC_____. (a)

In a similar manner, for very low frequency triggering signals (below

16 c/s) the TRIGGER COUPLING must be set to ____DC____. (b)

Given that the triggering signal is 5 + 2 sin 2πt, is it possible to

set the trigger coupling so that the trigger circuit only responds to

the AC component (2 sin 2πt) and not to the DC component (5)? __YES__ (c)

Explain. ____SETTING TO AC WILL BLOCK DC____.

BAD
QUESTION
SHOULD
SPECIFY
2πt or
ω < 16 c/s

85

(a) $K_c v_1$ (c) 1 div / 10 volts = .1 div/volt

(b) connect + side of v_1 to both +INPUT and -INPUT (center terminals) connect the oscillator ground to the scope ground (with this connection $v+ = v- = v_1$)

3.42 $v_1 = 5 \sin \omega t$ is connected to both the +INPUT and the -INPUT on the vertical amplifier. A peak deflection of 2 divisions is observed, so K_c = _____.   (a)

The scope is set to S_v = .01 volts/div, so K_d = _____.   (b)

Therefore, the common-mode rejection ratio is _____.   (c)

4.37 Sketch the trace approximately for each of the following values of θ:

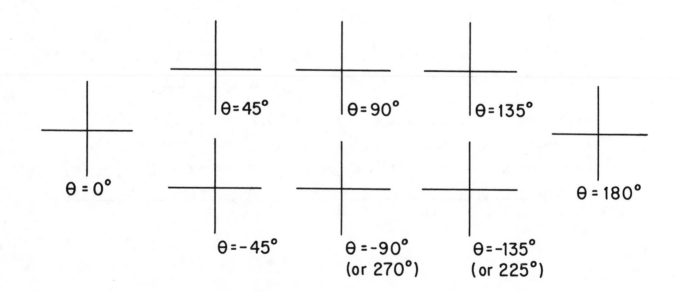

(a) 0 (since no DC current can flow through the capacitor)

(b) $v_{AC}(t)$ (since the AC voltage across the capacitor is negligible)

1.42 In the preceding circuit, C is referred to as a blocking capacitor
because it blocks the _____DC_____ and passes only   (a)
the _____AC_____.   (b)

(a) DC   (b) DC

(c) No, because DC coupling must be used for signals below 16 c/s.

2.42 If TRIGGER LEVEL = 0, TRIGGER SLOPE = +, circle and label the points on the
following waveform at which triggering will occur (a) for AC coupling and
(b) for DC coupling.

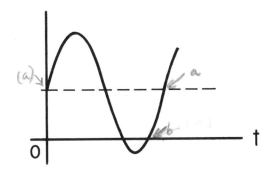

Note: In this and the following figures, the dashed line is the average
value (DC value) of the waveform. If you need to review AC and DC components, turn to page 212.

(a) 2/5 = .4 div/volt   (b) 1/.01 = 100 div/volt

(c) 100/.4 = 250

3.43 The following procedure can be used to determine the common-mode rejection ratio:

1. Adjust the oscillator output for a peak voltage V_p.

2. Then connect the oscillator to the scope and observe the peak deflection y_1 for a sensitivity setting S_v. Show the required connections:

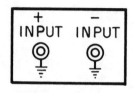

(a)

3. Calculate the CMRR in terms of V_p, y_1, and S_v using the following equations:

_____   _____   _____ (b)

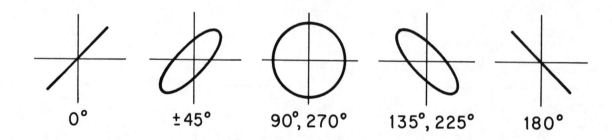

| 0° | ±45° | 90°, 270° | 135°, 225° | 180° |

4.38 Fill in the number of the ellipse which corresponds to each value of θ:

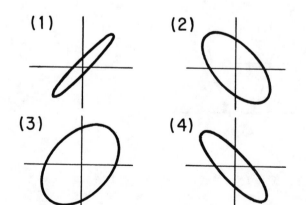

θ	ellipse number	
± 15		(a)
± 70		(b)
± 155	*	(c)
± 130	*	(d)

*Be careful. Think before you write your answer.

88

(a) DC component   (b) AC component

1.43 The scope amplifiers are direct-coupled and pass signals of all frequencies from DC to a certain maximum frequency limit. In some applications, the signal to be observed with the scope has both AC and DC components. If we are only interested in observing the AC component, it is necessary to block the _____ DC _____ with a   (a)

_____ capacitor _____ .   (b)

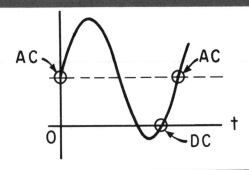

2.43 Do not confuse the effect of the AC-DC vertical input switch with the effect of the AC-DC trigger coupling switch.

Trigger source is set to INT.

The following waveform appears on the screen with the vertical input set to DC and with AC trigger coupling:

For this observed waveform the trigger slope is ___+___   (a)
and the trigger level is ___0___ .   (b)

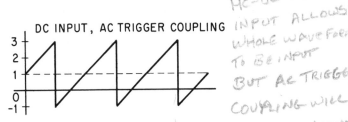

The vertical input is now changed to AC. The sweep will trigger at the same point in time because __AC COMPONENT__ (c)
__SAME IN BOTH__

Sketch the new waveform observed on the screen.   (d)

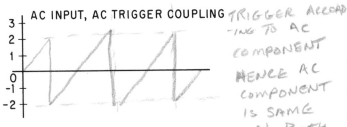

APPARENTLY AC-DC VERT INPUT ALLOWS WHOLE WAVEFORM TO BE INPUT BUT AC TRIGGER COUPLING WILL TRIGGER ACCORD-ING TO AC COMPONENT HENCE AC COMPONENT IS SAME IN BOTH (a)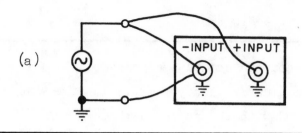

(b) $K_d = 1/S_v$, $K_c = y_1/V_p$

$$CMRR = K_d/K_c = V_p/y_1 S_v$$

3.44 If $S_v = .5$ and CMRR = 1000

$K_d = $ _____ and $K_c = $ _____ (a,b)

If $v_+ = 8$ and $v_- = 4$, the difference mode component is

$\Delta v = $ _____ and the common-mode component is $v_c = $ _____ (c,d)

The actual deflection would be _____ compared with (e)

_____ for an ideal differential amplifier. The per cent (f)

error in the deflection would be _____. (g)

(a) (1)   (b) (3)   (c) (4)   (d) (2)

4.39 What is the possible range for the magnitude of θ if the major axis

of the ellipse is tilted this way: ⟋   ? _____ $< |\theta| <$ _____ (a)

If the major axis is tilted the other way? _____ $< |\theta| <$ _____ (b)

Note: $|\theta|$ is always a positive number. If $|\theta| = 15°$, then

$\theta = $ _____ or _____. (c)

(a) DC component   (b) blocking capacitor

1.44 A typical input arrangement to the vertical amplifier is shown in
Fig. 1-44. R represents the impedance seen at the input terminals of
the vertical amplifier and C is a blocking capacitor. When the AC
input is selected, the scope input is coupled to the amplifier input
through a ___blocking capacitor___.   (a)

If S_V = 1 volt/div, the DC input is selected, and the scope input

voltage is v_V = 3 volts DC, the vertical deflection will be

___3___ divisions.   (b)

If the input is now switched to AC input, the blocking capacitor will

charge up to ___3___ volts, v_V' will become ___0___ volts,   (c,d)

and the vertical deflection will be ___0___ divisions.   (e)

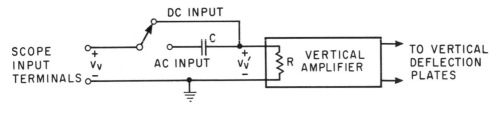

DC INPUT

SCOPE
INPUT
TERMINALS v_V AC INPUT v_V' R   VERTICAL
AMPLIFIER   TO VERTICAL
DEFLECTION
PLATES   C

FIG. 1-44

(a) +   (b) 0
(c) the AC component is the
     same in both cases   (d)

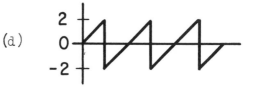

2.44 The following waveform is observed
with the vertical input set to DC
and with AC trigger coupling.

Now the trigger coupling is switched
to DC (leaving everything else
unchanged). The waveform does <u>not</u>
shift up or down because

___VERTICAL INPUT STAYED AT___ (a)

___DC___

The waveform <u>does</u> shift sideways
because ___TRIGGERING AT DC=0___

___TRIGGERING TIME DIFFERENT___ (b)

Sketch the new waveform as observed
on the screen.   (c)

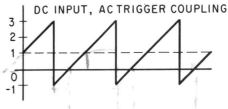

DC INPUT, AC TRIGGER COUPLING

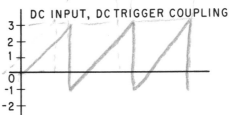

DC INPUT, DC TRIGGER COUPLING

(a) $1/.5 = 2$ (b) $2/1000 = .002$ (c) $8 - 4 = 4$

(d) $\frac{1}{2}(8 + 4) = 6$ (e) $K_d \Delta v + K_c v_c = 2 \times 4 + .002 \times 6 = 8.012$

(f) 8   (g) $(.012/8) \times 100\% = 0.15\%$

3.45 If $v_+ = 10.05$, $v_- = 10.00$, $S_v = .1$ volt/div, and the common-mode rejection ratio is 1000, the vertical deflection is

_____.   (a)

The per cent error in the deflection is _____.   (b)

When v_+ and v_- are very close together, a large error in the deflection is possible. The larger the common-mode rejection ratio, the

_____ will be the error.   (c)

(a) $0° < |\theta| < 90°$ (b) $90° < |\theta| < 180°$ (c) $+15°$ or $-15°$

4.40 We will now derive a method for finding the numerical value of θ from
the ellipse.

Let $x = A \sin \omega t$, $y = B \sin(\omega t + \theta)$

d_1, the peak-to-peak vertical deflection, is _____   (a)

Where the ellipse intersects the y-axis, $x = A \sin \omega t = 0$, so
$\omega t = 0$ or $180°$, and $y =$ _____ or _____.   (b)

d_2, the distance between the y-axis intercepts is _____   (c)

$d_2/d_1 =$ _____ $=$ _____   (d)

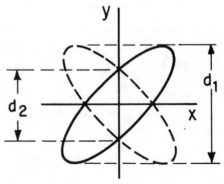

(a) blocking capacitor   (b) 3   (c) 3
(d) 0 (since no DC current is flowing, there is no voltage across R) (e) 0

1.45 In the figure below, suppose that $v_v = 10 + 5 \sin \omega t$. If the DC
(direct-coupled) input is selected, $v_v' =$ ___10 + 5 sin ωt___ (a)
Assume that ω is high enough so that the AC impedance of the capacitor
is negligible compared with R. If the AC input is selected, C will
charge up to 10 volts, and $v_v' =$ ___5 sin ωt___. (b)

If $S_v = 5$ volts/div and the AC input is used, the vertical deflection
will be between the limits ___1 division up___ and ___1 division down___. (c)

If $S_v = 5$ volts/div and the DC input is used, the vertical deflection
will be between the limits ___+3 div___ and ___-1 div___. (d)

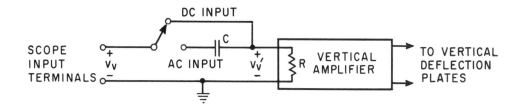

SCOPE INPUT TERMINALS — DC INPUT — AC INPUT — v_v' — R VERTICAL AMPLIFIER — TO VERTICAL DEFLECTION PLATES

(a) the DC component of the input
is unchanged

(b) the sweep triggers at a different
time

(c)

2.45 When using internal trigger source and DC trigger coupling, the entire output of the vertical amplifier, <u>including the DC component added by the
position control</u> is fed into the triggering circuit. In other words, for
DC trigger coupling the point at which triggering occurs is determined by
the voltage level of the waveform as it appears on the screen rather than
by the voltage level of the input waveform.

With AC trigger coupling, + slope, 0 trigger level, and the vertical input
voltage equal to $4 \sin \omega t$, the position control is adjusted so that the
following waveform appears on the screen. Sketch the waveform which will
appear when trigger coupling is changed to DC.

must be using INT. TRIGG

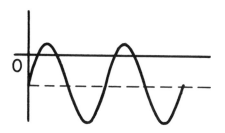   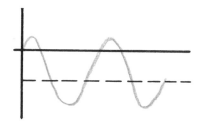

(a) .6 div   (b) 20%   (c) smaller

3.46 Even when the difference of the two inputs is small, the maximum voltage which can be applied to either the +INPUT or the -INPUT must be
limited to avoid overloading the scope amplifier and distorting the
signal. The limits are given in Table 5-1 (p. 214).

If S_v = 10 mv/div., what is the maximum allowable input voltage?

_____   (a)

When only one input is used, if the vertical deflection of the spot is
such that it remains on the screen we know that the maximum input
voltage has not been exceeded. Is this statement true when both + and
- inputs are used? _____. Explain. _____ (b)

_____

_____

(a) 2B (since the peak value of y is B)   (b) B sin θ or -B sin θ
(c) 2B sin θ   (d) $\dfrac{2B \sin \theta}{2B}$ = sin θ

4.41 Give a formula for computing $|\theta|$ in terms of distances which can be
measured on the ellipse. $|\theta|$ = _____   (a)
Show these distances on the ellipses below.

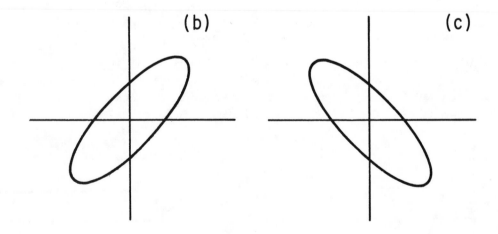

(b)   (c)

94

(a)　10 + 5 sin ωt　　(b)　5 sin ωt　　(c)　+1 and -1 div

(d)　+3 and +1 div (since maximum v_v is 10 + 5(1) and minimum v_v is 10 + 5(-1)

1.46　If the input signal contains both AC and DC components, we should use
the AC input if we want to observe the ＿＿＿＿＿Ac＿＿＿＿＿＿ only,　　(a)
but we should use the DC input if we want to observe both the

＿＿＿＿＿＿AC & DC＿＿＿＿＿＿＿＿＿.　　　　　　　　　　　(b)

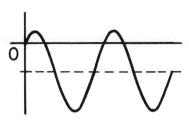

2.46　The spot will stay at the left edge of the screen until the sweep is triggered.　When the spot is not moving across the screen, the intensity is
automatically reduced so the spot cannot be seen.　We say that the spot is
"blanked out" when it is not moving across the screen from left to right.

For the sweep waveform shown below, plot the corresponding spot intensity
as a function of time.　(Your plot should show at what times the spot is
normal intensity and at what times it is blanked out.)

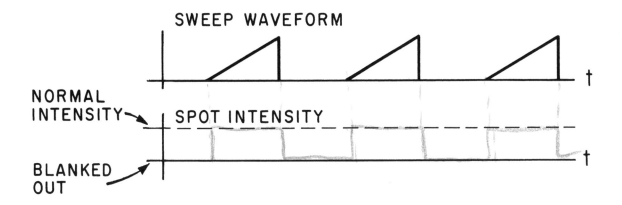

(a) 561: 5 volts   503: 2 volts

(b) No. The difference of the inputs and the deflection may be small even if the maximum input voltage is exceeded.

3.47 If the maximum input voltage is exceeded at either input, the signal may be badly distorted. If $v_+ = 8 \sin \omega t$ and $v_- = 8.5 \sin \omega t$, the smallest VOLTS/DIV setting which can be used without danger of distorting the signal is _____. The corresponding <u>peak-to-peak</u> (a)
deflection is _____. (Assume that the common-mode (b)
rejection ratio is very high.)

Note: peak-to-peak is two times peak.

(a) $|\theta| = \sin^{-1}(d_2/d_1)$

(b,c) d_1 is the distance between the top and bottom of the ellipse.

d_2 is the distance between the y-axis intercepts.

4.42 The above formula gives a value of $|\theta|$ between 0 and 90° and a second value between 90 and 180°. How do we tell which value is correct?

_____ (a)

If we change the vertical gain of the scope, will this change the value of $|\theta|$ which is computed by the formula? _____

Explain. _____ (b)

(a) AC component (b) AC and DC components

At very low frequencies, the impedance of the blocking capacitor
$(1/\omega C)$ is <u>not</u> negligible compared with the input impedance of the
amplifier (R). Therefore, at very low frequencies, the voltage drop
across the _____ *capacitor* _____ is not negligible, and the (a)
AC input (should/should not) _____ *should not* _____ be used. (b)

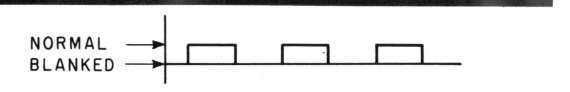

NORMAL
BLANKED

At very high sweep rates, the time required to reset the sweep generator is
no longer negligible as it is at slower sweep rates. The sweep waveform
and the corresponding spot intensity are shown below for a very high sweep
rate:

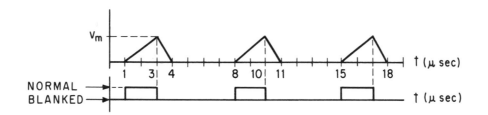

If v_m is the voltage required to deflect the spot 10 divisions, what
is the sweep rate? _____ *2/10 = .2* _____ μ sec/div (a)
In the above example, how much time does it take to reset the sweep
generator to 0? _____ *1 μsec* _____ (b)
Can the spot be seen when it is returning from the right side of the
screen to the left? _____ *No* _____ (c)

(a) .5 (.2 volts/div couldn't be used since the input is greater than
5 volts)

(b) 2(8.5 - 8)/.5 = 2 div.

3.48 The vertical amplifier is used as a differential amplifier with

+INPUT = .2 sin 100t + .5 cos 1000t

-INPUT = .2 sin 100t

If the volts/div setting is .1, what will the vertical deflection be
is the amplifier is ideal?   y = _____ (a)

What will it be if the common-mode rejection ratio is 100?

y = _____ (b)

(a) from the slope of the major axis of the ellipse

(b) NO, because d_2 and d_1 change in the same ratio.

4.43 For each of the ellipses below, compute the two possible values of θ.

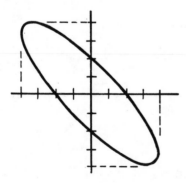 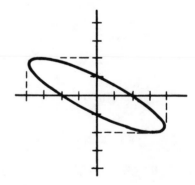

$|\theta| = \sin^{-1}$ _____ = _____

θ = _____ or _____ θ = _____ or _____

(a)   (b)

98

(a) blocking capacitor   (b) should not

1.48 If our input signal contains only an AC component and the frequency
is high enough so that the impedance of the blocking capacitor $(1/\omega C)$
is small compared with the input impedance (R), we (should use the
DC input/should use the AC input/can use either the AC or DC input)

_____ *can use either* _____ . At very low frequencies,   (a)

we must use the ___ *DC* ___ to observe an AC signal, because   (b)

___ *voltage drop at low freq on cap, & impedance is* ___   (c)
not negligible

(a) $\dfrac{2\mu sec}{10 \text{ div}} = .2 \ \mu sec/div$

(b) 1 μsec (between 3 and 4 μsec, 10 and 11 μsec, etc.)

(c) NO. (The spot is blanked out during the time the sweep generator is
resetting.)

THIS IS A GOOD PLACE TO TAKE A BREAK

Auto Triggering

2.48 The TRIGGER LEVEL control has a position marked AUTO (automatic triggering). When set to AUTO, the sweep will be triggered automatically
at regular intervals even when no triggering signal is present.

If the TRIGGER SOURCE is set to INTernal and no vertical input signal
is present, what should be observed on the screen if the LEVEL is <u>not</u>
set to AUTO? ___ *DOT ON SCREEN (NOTHING IS SEEN DOT NOT MOVING* ___   (a)

If the LEVEL is now switched to AUTO, what should be observed at low
sweep rates? ___ *DOT MOVING ACROSS SCREEN* ___   (b)

At high sweep rates? ___ *LINE (CAUSED BY DOT MOVING)* ___   (c)

(a) 5 cos 1000t   (b) 5 cos 1000t + .01 (2.5 cos 1000t + 2 sin 100t)

$$= 5.025 \cos 1000t + .02 \sin 100t$$

3.49 S_v is set to 2 volts/div. $v_+ = 60 \sin \omega t$ and $v_- = 54 \sin \omega t$

The peak-to-peak deflection should be _____ div.   (a)

If the waveform on the screen is distorted, what is the probable

cause? _____   (b)

What could be done to eliminate this distortion? _____

_____   (c)

Other than distortion, what problem might be encountered in using the

differential amplifier if v_+ and v_- have a large common mode component

and a small difference component? _____

_____   (d)

(a) $|\theta| = \sin^{-1} \frac{4}{8} = 150°$ (note that 30° is not correct because of the
                                             way the ellipse is tilted)

   $\theta = 150°$ or $-150°$ (since there is no way to tell the sign of
                                    the angle)

(b) $\theta = 150°$ or $-150°$ (the ratio of d_2 to d_1 is the same as in (a)).

4.44 When using the ellipse method, the horizontal position must be adjusted
very carefully so that the trace is exactly centered in the horizontal
direction.
Why?_____   (a)

Is it necessary to adjust the vertical position carefully so that the
trace is exactly centered in the vertical direction?_____   (b)
Explain_____

_____

(a) can use either AC or DC input

(b) DC

(c) the impedance of the blocking capacitor is not negligible

---

1.49 In which of the following cases will the trace be an ellipse
(or circle)?___(1) (3)_____ (a)

In which cases will the trace be a diagonal line? ___(2) (4)_____ (b)

case (1): $v_v = 3 \sin \omega t$ $v_h = 4 \cos \omega t$

case (2): $v_v = 2 \cos \omega t$ $v_h = 5 \cos \omega t$

case (3): $v_v = 2 \cos \omega t$ $v_h = 5 \sin \omega t$

case (4): $v_v = 2 \sin \omega t$ $v_h = 4 \sin \omega t$

(a) Nothing. (The sweep is not triggered. The spot remains at the left
edge of the screen, but it is blanked out because it is not moving.)

(b) The spot will sweep across the screen.

(c) The moving spot will become a horizontal line.

2.49 When set to AUTO, the trigger level is not adjustable. When a triggering
signal is present, the sweep will trigger at a level near zero. Thus the
sweep will synchronize on AUTO if a proper triggering signal is present,
but we cannot control the level at which triggering occurs. In which of
the following situations is it permissible to use AUTO? _____

(a) We want to display a voltage waveform which has a magnitude of 5 volts
at t = 0. We want t = 0 to correspond to the left edge of the graticule.

(b) We wish to observe the shape of a voltage waveform, but we don't care
what point on the waveform corresponds to t = 0.

(c) We want to measure the peak-to-peak amplitude of a voltage waveform.

(d) We want the sweep to trigger when an external trigger signal is
exactly equal to 0.

(a) 6 div.   (b) input voltages v_+ and v_- are too large

(c) change to 5 volts/div range

(d) loss of accuracy because common-mode component is amplified and not completely rejected.

3.50 The vertical amplifier is set to .1 volt/div. Probes are connected to both the +INPUT and -INPUT on the differential amplifier, and 10 volts is applied to both probe inputs. If the attenuation of both probes is the same and the differential amplifier is ideal, the vertical deflection will be _____ (a)

Two probes will not have exactly the same attenuation. Suppose that the probe on the +INPUT attenuates the signal by a factor of 9.8 and the probe on the -INPUT by a factor of 10.2. The actual input voltage on the +INPUT will be _____ and on the -INPUT will be _____ (b)

Still assuming the differential amplifier itself is ideal, the vertical deflection will be _____ divisions. (c)

When the differential amplifier is used in the differential mode with mismatched probes, the effective CMRR (that is, the CMRR measured with respect to the probe input terminals) will be (larger/the same/smaller) _____ than the CMRR of the amplifier itself. (d)

(a) The value of distance between the y intercepts would change if the trace was shifted horizontally.

(b) No. Neither d_1 or d_2 changes when the trace is shifted up or down.

4.45 Compute accurately the value(s) of θ for each of the following ellipses:

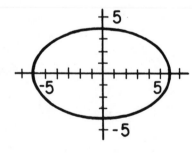

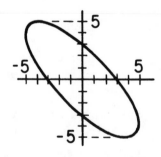

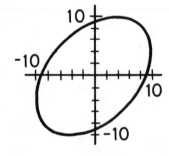

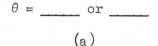 $\theta =$ _____ or _____

 $\theta =$ _____ or _____

 $\theta =$ _____ or _____

(a)

(b)

(c)

(a) 1 and 3   (b) 2 and 4

1.50 Sinusoidal voltages of the same frequency are applied to both the
vertical and horizontal scope inputs.

If the AC components of v_v and v_h are in phase, the trace will be
a(an)_____line_____.   (a)

If the AC components of v_v and v_h are 90° out of phase (i.e., one is
a sine and one is a cosine), the trace will be a(an)___circle or ellipse_
_____.   (b)

b and c

2.50 When the triggering level is set to AUTO, the triggering signal is
AC (AC SLOW for 561) coupled regardless of the setting of the trigger
coupling switch. In which of the following situations is it permissible to use AUTO? _____   (a)

yes (a) We want to ignore the DC component of the triggering signal.

no   (b) We want the DC component of the triggering signal to affect the
          level at which the sweep triggers.

yes (c) The triggering signal is a 2000 c/s sine wave.

no   (d) The triggering signal is a 2 c/s sine wave.
          (If in doubt about (d), reread frame 2.41.)

Which trigger control switch need not be set when the trigger LEVEL
is set to AUTO? ___TRIGGER COUPLING___   (b)

(a) 0 (since the amplifier is ideal and both inputs are the same)

(b) $v_+ = 10/9.8 = 1.02$ $v_- = 10/10.2 = .98$

(c) $y = (v_+ - v_-)/S_v = (1.02 - .98)/.1 = .4$ div

(d) smaller (because the common-mode signal is slightly different at the +INPUT and -INPUT it is not completely rejected)

3.51 Since the probes in the laboratory are not matched, is it desirable to use probes when using both the +INPUT and -INPUT on the differential amplifier? _____ Explain. _____ (a)

_____

The most sensitive range on the scope (without the probe) is 1 mv/div. If the signal being observed had an amplitude of 2 mv, would it be desirable to use the probe? _____ Explain. _____ (b)

_____

(a) $\pm 90°$ (b) $\pm 143°$ (c) $\pm 64°$

THIS IS A GOOD PLACE TO TAKE A BREAK

The Webb Mask

4.46 Since the thickness (D) of the ellipse varies with the angle θ, it is possible to determine θ from this thickness. Let us work out an example of this. Assume that the horizontal deflection is $x = 4 \sin \omega t$ and the vertical deflection is $y = 4 \sin (\omega t + \theta)$. The resulting trace is shown below. If the thickness is $D = 4\sqrt{2}$, compute the values of x and y which correspond to the point P on the ellipse. (Note that x is negative.)

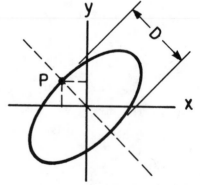

x = _____

y = _____ (a)

From the above value of x, compute the corresponding value of ωt = _____ (b)

From the above value of y, compute $\omega t + \theta$ and hence determine θ.

$\omega t + \theta$ = _____

θ = _____ degrees   (c)

Check your value of θ to see if it is reasonable considering the orientation and size of the ellipse. If it isn't, check your calculations.

(a) line

(b) ellipse (or circle if the amplitudes are equal)

1.51 If x = 2 + 3 cos ωt and y = 1 + 3 sin ωt

maximum x deflection = _____5_____ (a)

minimum x deflection = _____-1_____ (a negative number) (b)

maximum y deflection = _____4_____ (c)

minimum y deflection = _____-2_____ (also negative) (d)

Now sketch a rectangle on the screen showing the limiting values of the x and y deflections. The trace must lie within this rectangle.

Sketch the trace.

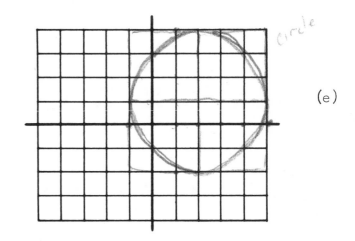

circle

(e)

(a) (a) and (c) only (the frequency is too low in (d))

(b) TRIGGER COUPLING

2.51 With no external signals connected either to the vertical input or to the external trigger input, we wish to observe a horizontal line on the scope. This can be accomplished by setting the TRIGGER LEVEL to _____ or by setting the TRIGGER SOURCE (a) to _____. (b)

A student connects a sine wave to the vertical input of the scope and finds that he cannot obtain a stable trace for any setting of the TRIGGER LEVEL control. Which of the triggering control switches is probably set wrong? _____ To what position should it be set? (c)

_____ (d)

(a) No, because mismatched probes would decrease the CMRR.

(b) No, because the deflection would be reduced to .2 div.

3.52 Check to indicate proper usage of the probe in each of the following situations:

	probe should be used	probe could be used if desired	probe should <u>not</u> be used
(a) low frequency signals			
(b) high frequency signals			
(c) low impedance circuits			
(d) high impedance circuits			
(e) very low amplitude signals			
(f) high amplitude signals			
(g) both +INPUT and -INPUT are being used (and common-mode signal is large)			
(h) only +INPUT is being used			

(a) $x = 2\sqrt{2} \cos 135° = -2 \quad y = 2\sqrt{2} \sin 135° = 2$

(b) $4 \sin \omega t = -2, \quad \omega t = -30°$

(c) $4 \sin(\omega t + \theta) = 2, \quad \omega t + \theta = 30° \quad \theta = 60°$

4.47 The Webb mask, which consists of a transparent overlay of the form shown in Fig. 4-47 (next page) provides a convenient way of measuring the thickness of the ellipse. This mask is placed over the scope screen so that the ellipse may be viewed through it. If the <u>major</u> axis of the ellipse lies along line M-M' on the mask, the possible range for $|\theta|$ will be _____ to _____. (a)

If it lies along N-N' the range for $|\theta|$ will be _____ to _____. (b)

(In answering this question, ignore the numbers printed on the mask.)

(a) 5   (b) -1

(c) 4   (d) -2   (e)

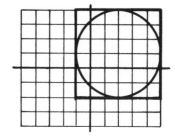

1.52 Let x = -1 + 3 cos ωt   y = 1 + 2 cos ωt

The trace will be a(an) _____*line*_____ between the points   (a)

x = __2__, y = __3__   and   x = __-4__, y = __-1__   (b)

(a) AUTO   (b) LINE   (c) SOURCE   (d) INTernal

Review Problems

2.52 The trigger controls are set as follows:

        LEVEL = 0, SLOPE = +, SOURCE = INTernal,
        TIME/DIV = .05 sec/div.

The vertical input is a 1 c/s sine wave.
The TRIGGER COUPLING should be set to _____.   (a)
How many cycles will appear on the screen? _____.   (b)
If you want 2 cycles of the same sine wave to appear, to what value
should TIME/DIV be changed? _____   (c)

Probe should be used in (b) and (d) to prevent loading the circuit.

Probe should <u>not</u> be used in (e) and (g).

Other cases are optional.

3.53 You have now completed Preparation Part III. You should understand some of the sources of errors which occur when the scope is used to make accurate measurements, and you should know how to avoid these errors. You should know how to use the probe and the differential amplifier. Now go to the lab and do Lab Part III.

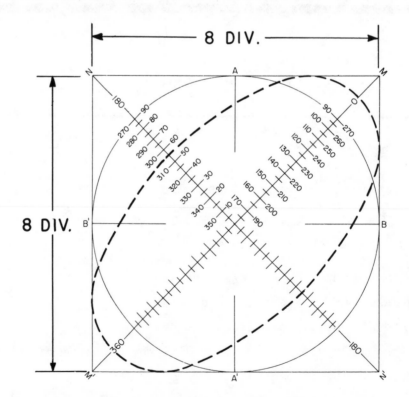

FIG. 4-47. HEWLETT PACKARD WEBB MASK
Reproduced from HEWLETT-PACKARD Application Note No. 29 and
used by permission of HEWLETT-PACKARD COMPANY.

(a) line   (b) (x = 2, y = 3) and (x = -4, y = -1)

Review Problems

1.53 $S_h = S_v = 1$ volt/div

The vertical amplifier is set to AC and the horizontal amplifier is direct coupled. The input voltages are

$$v_v = 2 + 2 \sin \omega t$$

$$v_h = 2 + 2 \cos \omega t$$

Assume that ω is high enough so the blocking capacitor does not affect the AC component.

Sketch the trace which will appear on the screen.

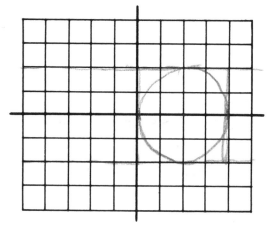

(a) DC (since the frequency of the triggering signal is very low)
(b) 1/2   (c) .2 sec/div

2.53 v_1 is connected to the external trigger input and v_2 to the vertical input. The trigger controls are set as follows: SOURCE = EXTernal, SLOPE = +, LEVEL = 0, TIME/DIV = .05 ms/div, COUPLING = AC (AC SLOW for 561).

The vertical sensitivity is 5 volts/div. Sketch the pattern which appears on the screen. Work this problem carefully; don't guess. Label the trace which appears the first time the sweep is triggered and the one which appears the second time.

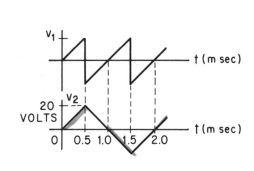

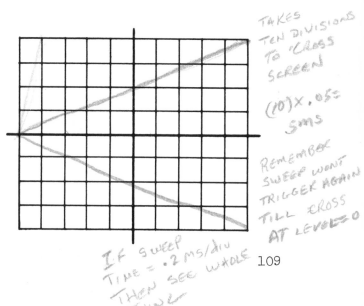

TAKES TEN DIVISIONS TO CROSS SCREEN

(10) X .05 = 5 MS

REMEMBER SWEEP WONT TRIGGER AGAIN TILL CROSS AT LEVEL = 0

IF SWEEP TIME = .2 MS/div THEN SEE WHOLE THING

109

LABORATORY PART III

3.54 In this part you will learn how to check the calibration of the scope so that it can be used to make accurate measurements. You will learn how to operate the remaining scope controls which have not been discussed in Parts I and II. The loading effect of the scope on the voltage being measured will be investigated, and the use of the probe will be introduced to reduce this loading effect.

In addition to your scope you will need the following equipment:

       sine wave oscillator (HP 200AB or CD or equivalent)
       low voltage power supply (HP 721A or equivalent)
       10X attenuating probe (Tektronix P6006 or equivalent)
       matched pair of precision resistors (each about 500 kilohms)
       two coaxial cable leads, each with a connector to fit your scope
          on one end and red and black clips on the other end

For frames 3.92 to 3.100 you will also need

       adaptor plug to change 3-prong line plug to 2-prong plug
       1 kilohm, 10 kilohm, 100 kilohm, and 1 megohm resistors

After taking the necessary precaution, turn on your scope so it will be warmed up when you are ready to use it.

(a) 0 to 90°   (b) 90 to 180°

(Note that these answers are not directly related to the markings on the axis.)

4.48 The mask is calibrated so that the angle in degrees may be read directly without the necessity of making calculations. Before reading the angle, the signal amplitudes and scope gain must be adjusted so that the peak-to-peak vertical deflection is 8 divisions and the peak-to-peak horizontal deflection is the same. If the trace is properly adjusted, what will be seen if the horizontal signal is removed and only the vertical signal is present? _____

_____ (use letters from Fig. 4-47 in your answer).   (a)

If only the horizontal signal is present? _____   (b)

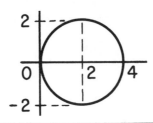

1.54 S_v = .05 volts/div, S_h = 2 volts/div, the horizontal input is 10 sin ωt and the vertical input is .1 + .1 sin ωt.   (Note that v_v and v_h are in phase.) Sketch the trace which will appear on the screen if
      (a) the vertical AC input is used
      (b) the vertical DC input is used

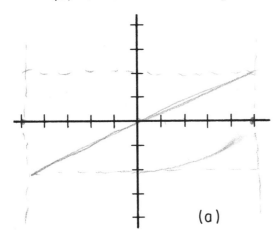

(a)

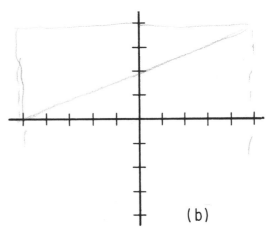

(b)

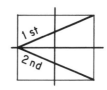

2.54 v_v is applied to the vertical input with the scope set as follows: vert. input to DC, trigger source to INT, trigger slope to - (negative), trigger coupling to DC, trigger level set to trigger when input voltage equals 1 volt, time/div to 0.5 ms, and volts/div to 0.5.

  (a) Sketch the sweep waveform.

  (b) Sketch the waveform which appears on the screen.

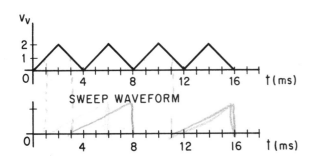

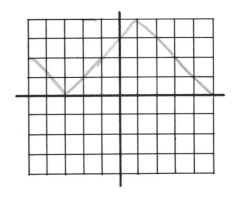

3.55 With no inputs connected to the scope, adjust your scope to obtain a properly focused, centered horizontal line on the screen. (How should you set TRIGGER LEVEL to trigger the sweep when there is no input?)

Now connect the sine-wave oscillator to the scope and display about 10 or 20 cycles of a 100 c/s sine wave with the vertical sensitivity set to 2 volts/div (calibrated). (How can you tell when the red knob is in the calibrated position?)

(a) line from A to A'   (b) line from B to B'

4.49 When the trace is properly adjusted, the phase angle may be read directly from the intersection of the ellipse with the scale on the mask. For the dashed ellipse of Fig. 4-47, $\theta = \underline{\hspace{1cm}}$ or $\underline{\hspace{1cm}}$ (a)

When the trace is properly adjusted, what relation does the ellipse bear to all four sides of the outer square (MN'M'N)?

$\underline{\hspace{6cm}}$ (b)

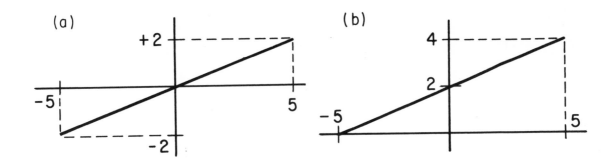

(a) (b)

1.55 You have now completed Preparation Part I and should understand the types
of deflections produced by various signals applied to the vertical and
horizontal inputs. Before continuing, go back and review any frames which
you missed. Then to to the laboratory and perform Laboratory Part I.

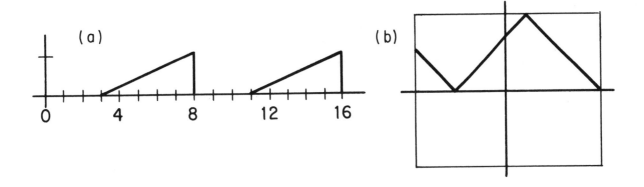

(a) (b)

2.55 This completes Preparation Part II. You should now understand how to display a waveform on the scope as a function of time. You should understand
the functions of the TRIGGER SLOPE, LEVEL, SOURCE, and COUPLING controls on
the TIME BASE.

Now go to the lab and do Laboratory Part II.

<u>Sweep Magnifier</u>

3.56

561
ONLY

Any portion of the trace can be expanded horizontally five times by pulling out the red VARIABLE control knob on the Time Base. To expand any portion of the trace, move the portion to be expanded to the center of the screen and pull out the VARIABLE control knob. Try this.

When the sweep magnifier is on, to determine the true value of time/div (multiply/divide) _____the setting of   (a)
the TIME/DIV switch by _____.   (b)

503
ONLY

The trace can be expanded horizontally 2 to 50 times by setting the Horizontal Display switch to the appropriate position. With about 10 or 20 cycles of a 100 c/s sine wave on the screen try various "Sweep Magnified" positions on the switch.

When the sweep magnifier is being used, the spot travels (faster/slower) _____ across the screen, so to get the true value of   (c)
time/div we must (multiply/divide) _____ the setting of   (d)
the TIME/DIV switch by the magnifier setting.

(a) 55° or 305°   (b) it is tangent

4.50

Referring to Fig. 4-50 (p. 199), what adjustments (if any) must be made in each case before reading the phase angle from the Webb mask?
Fig. 4-50a _____
Fig. 4-50b _____
Fig. 4-50c _____
Fig. 4-50d _____

On Fig. 4-47, sketch the trace which should be seen when $\theta = 150°$.   (e)

LABORATORY PART I

1.56 Select a position in the lab which is equipped with a Tektronix 503, 561, 561A or 561B oscilloscope. You will also need the following equipment to provide signals to the scope:

(a) low voltage power supply for DC signals (HP 721A or equivalent)

(b) low-frequency function generator for sine, triangular and square waves (HP 202A or equivalent)

(c) a coaxial cable lead with a connector to fit the vertical input on your scope on one end and clips with red and black insulators on the other end

If the above equipment is not already at your position, obtain it from your lab instructor or supervisor. He will demonstrate the proper way to operate this equipment. Also obtain a continuity tester and an R-C network from the supervisor. Other necessary leads should be available in the laboratory.

Have you completed Preparation Part I? _____

LABORATORY PART II

2.56 In Lab Part I you operated the scope only with an external horizontal input. In this part you will use the TIME BASE to generate a horizontal sweep signal. You will learn how to display periodic waveforms on the screen, and you will also learn how to adjust the triggering controls. In addition to the scope and scope cables, you will need the following equipment:

(a) low voltage DC power supply

(b) low frequency function generator

(c) sine-wave oscillator (HP 200AB or HP 200 CD or equivalent)

Have you completed Preparation Part II? _____

(a) divide (since the spot moves faster, there is less time per division)

(b) 5   (c) faster   (d) divide

3.57

561
ONLY

If the sweep magnifier is used, the fastest possible sweep rate is

_____ microseconds/div.   (a)

503
ONLY

The maximum <u>calibrated</u> sweep rate is 0.1 microseconds/cm.

List three ways to obtain this sweep rate:

sweep time/cm switch setting	sweep magnifier setting
_____	_____
_____	_____
_____	_____

(b)

(a) increase horiz. gain   (b) increase vert. gain

(c) increase both vert. and horiz. gain   (d) adjust vert. position

(e) Your ellipse should have its major axis on N-N'; it should be tangent
     to all four sides of the square; it should intersect the scale at 150°.

4.51 In the given network, v_1 and v_2 do <u>not</u> have a common ground terminal. The
phase angle of v_2 with respect to v_1 is to be measured by the Webb mask.
Indicate the proper connections to the scope.

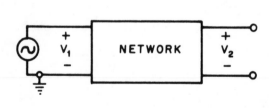

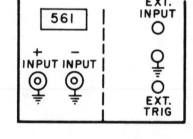

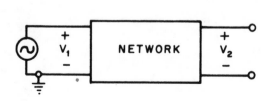

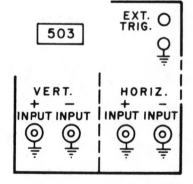

If your answer is NO, complete the preparation before proceeding.

Familiarization with the Scope

1.57   This programmed text is designed to be used with several types of oscilloscopes. Skip over parts which do not apply to the scope you are working with.

Sections marked "561 ONLY" apply only to the Tektronix 561, 561A or 561B oscilloscope.

Sections marked "503 ONLY" apply only to the Tektronix 503 oscilloscope. Unmarked sections apply to both types.

Turn to frame 1.58 unless you have a 503 scope.

503 ONLY   Examine the controls located on the lower part of the front panel of the scope. Controls for the VERTICAL amplifier are on the _____ and those for the HORIZONTAL amplifier are on the _____ .   (a) (b)

If your answer is NO, go back and complete the preparation before proceeding.

Triggering the Sweep

2.57   (a) What is the source of the triggering signal when the TRIGGER SOURCE is set to INTernal? _____

to LINE? _____

to EXTernal? _____

(b) Explain the difference between AC and DC TRIGGER COUPLING

_____

_____

(c) What is the effect of the TRIGGER SLOPE control?

_____

_____

(d) What is the effect of the TRIGGER LEVEL control?

_____

_____

117

(a) 0.2 μsec/div (1 μsec/div divided by 5)

(b) 1 μsec, X10; 2 μsec, X20; 5 μsec, X50

3.58 561: With the sweep magnifier on and TIME/DIV set to 1 ms, the following trace is observed:

503: With the sweep magnifier set to X5 and TIME/CM to 1 ms, the following trace is observed:

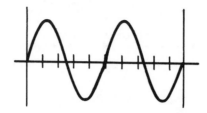

What is the frequency of the signal applied to the vertical input?

After writing your answer, verify it by observation.

Turn the sweep magnifier off.

---

v_1+ to horiz. EXT INPUT (+INPUT for 503)

v_2+ to vert. +INPUT, v_2- to vert. -INPUT

oscillator ground to scope ground

4.52 Summary: Two basic methods for measuring the phase angle of a voltage v_2 with respect to a reference voltage v_1 have been studied.

1. The <u>triggered sweep</u> method consists of two steps:

   a. Using v_1 as an external trigger input and as the vertical input, display v_1 as a function of time and calibrate the time axis for 20°/division (or some other convenient value).

   b. Without disturbing the trigger circuit, change the vertical input to v_2 and observe the phase difference.

2. The <u>ellipse</u> method consists of the following steps:

   a. Display v_2 vs v_1 on the screen.

   b. Compute the phase angle from the ratio of distances measured on the resulting ellipse. (The angle may also be read directly by using a Webb mask.)

(a) left   (b) right

1.58	The Tektronix 561 (or 561A or 561B) oscilloscope has two interchangeable plug-in units. The vertical plug-in is on the <u>left</u> side and the horizontal plug-in is on the <u>right</u> side. For your scope, the horizontal plug-in is TYPE _____ and the vertical plug-in is TYPE _____ .

561 ONLY

(a)

(b)

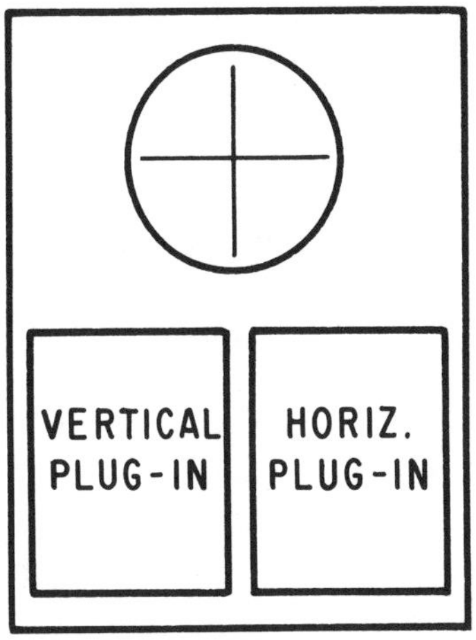

VERTICAL PLUG-IN   HORIZ. PLUG-IN

(a) from the vertical amplifier output; from the 60 c/s AC line; from the external trigger input

(b) On AC, trigger circuit responds to AC component of triggering signal only; on DC, trigger circuit responds to entire triggering signal.

(c) determines whether triggering occurs on positive or negative slope of triggering signal

(d) determines the voltage level at which triggering occurs

2.58	What precaution should be taken before turning on the scope?

_____ (a)

Take this precaution and explain the reason for it.

_____

_____ (b)

1000 c/s (With the sweep magnifier on (X5), the sweep rate is 0.2 ms/div. The period of the wave is 5 div x .2 ms/div = 1 ms, so f = 1000 c/s.)

DC Balance

3.59 The scope amplifiers may have a small DC output voltage even when the inputs are grounded. The DC BALANCE control can be adjusted to eliminate this unwanted DC output. The DC BALANCE must be adjusted when the scope is used to measure small signals, especially for signals in the 1 to 50 millivolt range.

[561 ONLY--Make sure the AC STABILIZED switch on the vertical amplifier is turned off.]

With the vertical amplifier inputs grounded, obtain a centered horizontal line on the screen. Does this trace move when the VOLTS/DIV switch is rotated from the high end to the low end? _____

LABORATORY PART IV

4.53 In this part you will measure the phase shift of a network at different frequencies using first the triggered sweep method and then the ellipse method. The results obtained by the two methods should agree closely if you work carefully. You will need the following equipment:

$\left\{ \begin{array}{c} \text{Tektronix} \\ \text{503 scope} \end{array} \right\}$ or $\left\{ \begin{array}{l} \text{Tektronix 561A (or 561) scope with 2A63 (or 63)} \\ \text{differential amplifier and 2B67 (or 67) time} \\ \text{base plug-in; 10,000-ohm potentiometer; for} \\ \text{frames 4.85 and 4.86 you will also need two} \\ \text{3A75 plug-ins or a second 2A63 (or 63) plug-in} \end{array} \right\}$

lattice phase shift network;   Webb mask
sine wave oscillator (HP 200AB or 200CD or equivalent)

Record the identification numbers on the back of the phase shift network and on the oscillator in Table 4-1 (p. 201). Use the same network and oscillator throughout Lab Part IV. You will use Table 4-1 to keep a record of phase shift measurements made by different methods so that you can easily check your answers.

Turn on the equipment so it will be warmed up when you are ready to use it.

(a) 2B67 or 67 [If you have a different plug-in type in the horizontal (right) channel, ask the supervisor to change plug-ins.]

(b) 2A63 or 63. [If you have a different plug-in type in the vertical (left) channel, ask the supervisor to change plug-ins.]

1.59 The scope has a 3-wire line cord. Two of the wires supply AC power to the scope and the third wire is a safety ground. The third wire is connected directly to the scope case and chassis. When the scope is plugged in, the scope case is connected to the building ground through the 3-wire line cord. Examine the line plug and use the continuity tester to verify that the round grounding pin is connected to the scope case. (The front panel of the scope is coated with non-conducting paint.) When the scope is plugged in, is it possible to have a high voltage between the scope case and the building ground? _____ Explain. (a)

_____. (b)

You should have turned down the intensity control because a high intensity spot would burn the screen.

2.59 (a) Turn the scope ON, and allow it to warm up.

(b) Ground the vertical inputs. (Use the AC-DC-GND switches).

561 ONLY {

(c) Set SWEEP MODE to NORMAL (2B67 Time Base only).

(d) To what position should the TIME/DIV switch be set if we want to see a stationary spot? _____

(e) Set the TIME/DIV switch to this position and obtain a centered spot, properly focused.

503 ONLY {

(f) To what position should the HORIZONTAL DISPLAY switch be set if we want to see a stationary spot? _____

(g) Set the HORIZONTAL DISPLAY to this position and obtain a centered spot, properly focused.

(h) To what position should the TRIGGER LEVEL control be set if we want the sweep to trigger when there is no triggering signal present?

_____

(i) Set the TRIGGER LEVEL to this position.

If your answer is YES, the vertical DC BALANCE is out of adjustment. If
no movement was observed, turn the DC BALANCE about 1/2 turn, and then
observe the effect of rotating the VOLTS/DIV switch.

3.60 To adjust the DC BALANCE for the vertical amplifier so that no motion of
the trace is observed when the VOLTS/DIV switch is rotated, use the following procedure:

(a) Set both input switches to GND and sensitivity to 0.2 volts/div
(calibrated). Center the trace with the position control.

(b) Rotate the sensitivity switch toward 1 mV/div. Use the DC BALANCE if
required to keep the trace on the screen. With the switch set to
1 mV/div, center the trace with the DC BALANCE.

(c) Check to see that there is no motion of the trace when the VOLTS/DIV
switch is rotated from one end to the other. If there is, repeat
(a) and (b).

Note: Wait at least five minutes after turning on the scope before
adjusting the DC BALANCE. Final adjustment of DC BALANCE
should be made after the scope is thoroughly warmed up--at
least 20 minutes after turning it on.

Did you turn down the intensity before you turned the scope on?
If you didn't, turn it down quickly before it is too late.

Phase Measurement by the Triggered Sweep Method

4.54 In order to obtain accurate results when using the triggered sweep method,
the time axis of the scope must be carefully calibrated. For each pair of
traces below, check the one which should give the most accurate results.

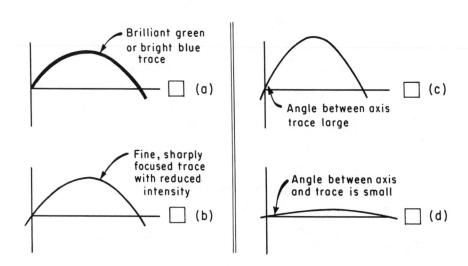

(a) no   (b) The scope case is connected to the building ground by the
          line cord.

1.60 Examine the scope and locate the input terminals shown below in Fig. 1.60.

Using the continuity tester, determine if ground terminal 1 is connected
directly to each of the following terminals (check if there is a connection):

ground terminal 2	outer conductor on +INPUT
ground terminal 3	outer conductor on -INPUT
scope case	grounding pin on line plug

Are all of the above terminals connected directly together? _____

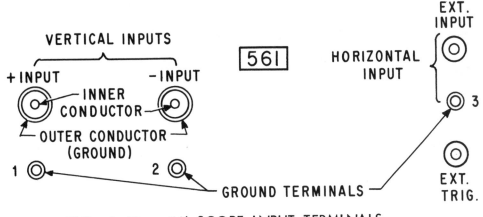

FIG. 1.60a. 561 SCOPE INPUT TERMINALS

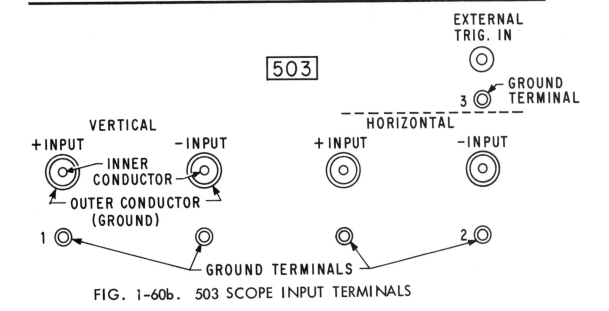

FIG. 1-60b. 503 SCOPE INPUT TERMINALS

TURN TO FRAME 2.60

3.61 Although the DC BALANCE control can be used to position the trace, it is NOT a position control and should NOT be used as such. If the DC BALANCE control is used as a position control, what undesirable effect would this have?

_____

_____ (a)

How can you tell when the DC BALANCE needs adjustment? _____

_____ (b)

Turn the DC BALANCE control 1 turn clockwise and verify your answer.

561
ONLY
{ With the amplifier still unbalanced, set S_v to 1 mv/div and observe the effect of turning AC STABILIZED on and off. When AC STABILIZED is on, the trace is again _____ . (c)
Turn AC STABILIZED off again.

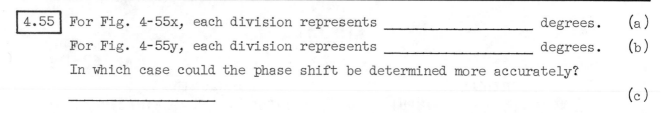

(b) is more accurate because a fine, sharply focused trace is easier to read
(c) is more accurate because the exact point at which the trace crosses the axis is easier to determine if the angle of crossing is large

---

4.55 For Fig. 4-55x, each division represents _____ degrees. (a)
For Fig. 4-55y, each division represents _____ degrees. (b)
In which case could the phase shift be determined more accurately?

_____ (c)

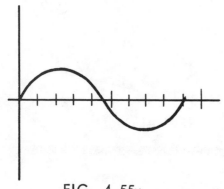

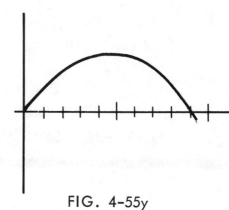

FIG. 4-55x   FIG. 4-55y

1.61 The line cord ground is <u>not</u> a reliable ground and should not be used to carry signals being observed on the scope. That is, always connect a separate ground wire directly to the signal source. The oscillator is being used to supply a signal to the scope in the diagram below. Assume that one side of the oscillator output is grounded to the building ground through its line cord.

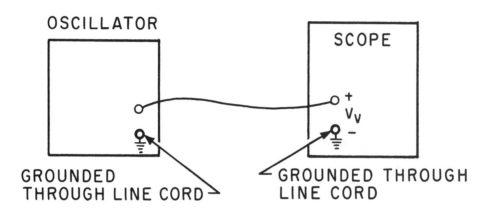

Draw a line to indicate what other connection (if any) should be made   (a)
in the above circuit. Would this connection be necessary if the line
cord grounds were perfect? _____   (b)

(d) EXT. INPUT   (f) HORIZ. AMPLIFIER (SWEEP DISABLED)

(h) AUTO (fully counterclockwise)

2.60 The sweep rate is adjustable by means of the black knob labeled TIME/DIV (SWEEP TIME/CM) and the red VARIABLE knob in the center. The calibrated sweep times apply only when the red knob is in the CALIBRATED position (rotated fully clockwise).

561 ONLY {
WARNING: The red knob on the TIME/DIV switch does <u>not</u> have a click stop in the CALIBRATED position like the red knob on the VOLTS/DIV switch. Do not try to force the red knob on TIME/DIV past the end of its normal rotation.

Try operating both red knobs and compare the difference in their operation.

On TIME/DIV, what <u>visual indication</u> is given when the red knob is not in the calibrated position? _____   (a)

On VOLTS/DIV, how can you tell when the red knob <u>is</u> in the calibrated position? _____   (b)
}

503 ONLY {
Try operating the red knob on the SWEEP TIME/CM switch and note that it works exactly like the red knob in the center of the SENSITIVITY switch.

On SWEEP TIME/CM, how can you tell when the red knob is in the calibrated position? _____   (c)
}

(a) The amplifier would be unbalanced, so it would be necessary to
     recenter the trace every time VOLTS/DIV was changed.

(b) The trace moves when VOLTS/DIV is rotated.

(c) centered (on the screen)

3.62 | Complete the following summary of the procedure for adjusting the DC
       BALANCE:

       After obtaining a horizontal line on the screen,

       (a) with S_V = _____, center the trace using the   (a)
                        _____ control.   (b)

       (b) with S_V = _____, center the trace using the   (c)
                        _____ control.   (d)

       (c) Repeat (a) and (b) if necessary.

561   ⎧ If you are measuring small AC signals and don't want to bother
ONLY ⎨ adjusting the DC BALANCE, what switch should be set to what
      ⎩ position? _____   (e)

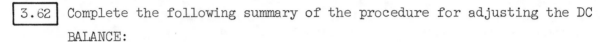

(a) 40°   (b) 20°   (c) Fig. 4.55y

4.56 | When the sweep is triggered, the exact starting point of the trace may be
       hard to see, especially at high sweep rates.

       Which of the two traces below will provide more accurate results when cali-
       brating the time axis? _____ (especially at high sweep rates)

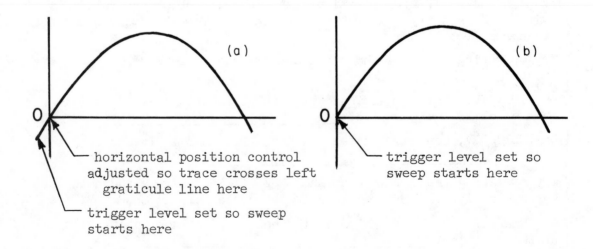

(a) connect a wire from the scope ground to the oscillator ground (since the line cord grounds are not reliable)

(b) NO

1.62   Burned spots appear on the scope screen as small, dark areas. Does your scope screen have any burned spots? _____   (a)

If your scope doesn't have any burned spots, look around the lab until you find one which does. This damage to the scope was caused by having the intensity set too _____ when the spot was   (b)

_____.   (c)

(a) The UNCAL light is on.
(b) The knob is past the click stop.
(c) The knob is past the click stop.

2.61   503 ONLY   { Set the Horizontal Display switch to SWEEP NORMAL (X1). This disconnects the Horizontal Input and connects the sweep generator to the horizontal amplifier.

Set the sweep rate to 2 sec/div (calibrated).

To move across the screen from the leftmost grid line to the rightmost grid line, the spot should take _____ sec.   (a)

ALL   { Use a watch to observe the time required for the spot to cross the screen. Observed time _____ sec.   (b)

(Note that the spot actually goes a little beyond the grid lines when it sweeps across. This is really of no concern since the calibrated sweep rates apply to divisions marked on the screen.)

(a) 0.2 volts/div   (b) position   (c) 1 mv/div

(d) DC BALANCE   (e) AC STABILIZED on

3.63 Now readjust the vertical DC BALANCE of the vertical amplifier without looking back at the procedure.   (a)

503 ⎰ Ground both the vertical and horizontal inputs, and set the scope
ONLY ⎱ to obtain a dot on the screen. Now adjust the DC BALANCE of the
       <u>horizontal</u> amplifier.   (b)

561 ⎰ The AC STABILIZED switch on the differential amplifier may be used
ONLY ⎱ to prevent the trace from drifting when measuring small AC signals
       in the 1 millivolt to 20 millivolt range. The AC STABILIZED switch
       must be off when using the DC input in this range. What warning is
       given when the AC STABILIZED switch is on and the input switch is
       in the DC position? _____ (c)

(a) is more accurate because it is easy to see the exact point at which
     the trace crosses the axis, but it is difficult to see the exact point
     at which the trace starts

4.57 The oscillator is not an ideal voltage source, but it has an internal
resistance. The equivalent circuit for the oscillator output is

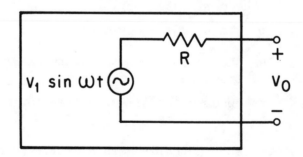

If a network is connected to the output terminals, the magnitude of v_o

will (increase/remain the same/decrease) _____ (a)

because _____ (b)

(b) high   (c) stationary (not moving)

1.63 As a precaution against burning the screen, always turn the <u>intensity</u> control all the way down (fully counterclockwise) <u>before</u> turning the scope on.

Take the necessary precaution against burning the screen, and then turn the scope ON so that it will be warmed up by the time you are ready to use it.

Also turn on the function generator (HP 202A) and DC power supply (HP 721A) so they will be warmed up when you need them. The screen is ruled off into divisions one centimeter square. The ruled portion of the entire screen is _____ cm by _____ cm. Each division is   (a) marked off into subdivisions along the axis. How many subdivisions are contained in each division? _____   (b)

(a) 20 sec. (2 sec/div x 10 div)
(b) If your answer is appreciably different from 20 seconds, ask your instructor to check the calibration of your time base.

2.62 If the spot takes 5 seconds to cross the screen, the sweep rate should be set at _____. After writing your answer, verify it experimentally.

(a,b) Check your adjustment by making sure that the trace doesn't move
       when VOLTS/DIV is rotated all the way from one end to the other
       (with AC STABILIZED OFF on 561).

(c) The AC STABILIZED light is on.

Calibration of the Vertical Amplifier Gain

3.64 If the scope is to be used to make accurate voltage measurements, the
      vertical amplifier must be properly calibrated. The scope has a
      built-in square wave source of voltage which you can use to check the
      calibration.

561 ONLY { The calibrator output is a square wave. The markings on the calibrat-
          or dial are peak-to-peak* volts. What is the range of peak-to-peak
          voltages available from the calibrator output?_____ (a)

503 ONLY { A square wave (approximately 350 c/s) is available between either of
          the calibrator output terminals and ground. The calibrator is marked
          in peak-to-peak* volts. The two available calibration voltages are
          _____ and _____ (peak-to-peak).   (b)

*May also be referred to as ground-to-peak since one peak is at 0 volts.

(a) decrease

(b) there will be a voltage drop across R
     (the network loads down the oscillator)

4.58 We will use a phase shift network of the following form:

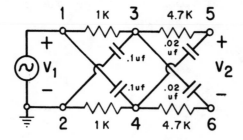

Express v_2 in terms of v_{52} (the voltage drop from terminal 5 to terminal 2) and v_{62}. $v_2 = $ _____ (a)

Would v_2 change if points 2 and 6 were both grounded? _____ (b)

Explain._____

1.64 Examine the block diagram of the scope (Fig. 1-64). The input to the horizontal amplifier may come from either the _____ (a) or the _____. (b)

In this part we will use an external horizontal input; the use of the sweep voltage from the TIME BASE will be explained in Part II.

503 ONLY { An external input to the horizontal amplifier may be used only when the sweep is disabled. Examine the HORIZONTAL DISPLAY switch on the scope and set it so that the horizontal input to the scope may come from an external source.

561 ONLY { The switch which connects the horizontal amplifier to the EXT. INPUT is located on the black TIME/DIV switch as shown. Set this switch so that the horizontal input may come from an external source.

TIME/DIV.

Time Base is Connected in these Positions

EXT. INPUT

Note: On concentric controls, the black panel markings refer to black knobs and the red panel markings to red knobs.

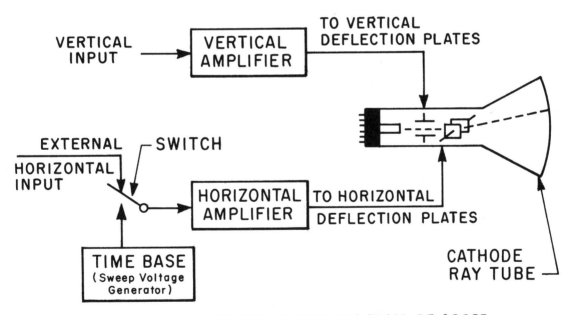

FIG. 1-64. SIMPLIFIED BLOCK DIAGRAM OF SCOPE

TURN TO FRAME 2.63

(a) 0.2 mv to 100 volts [for 561B, 4 mv to 40 volts]

(b) 5 mv and 500 mv

3.65 Select the 500 mv peak-to-peak calibrator output [400 mv for 561B],
connect it to the vertical input, and observe the calibrator waveform
(set +INPUT to DC and -INPUT to GND).

If a peak-to-peak deflection of 5 divisions [4 div for 561B] is desired,
the sensitivity switch should be set to _____ VOLTS/DIV   (a)
with the red variable knob in the _____ position.   (b)

After writing your answer, verify it by observation. (Ask the supervisor for the proper adaptor so that you can easily make connections
to the calibrator output.)

(a) $v_2 = v_{52} - v_{62}$

(b) Yes. There would be a short circuit between 6 and 2.

4.59 Obtain a centered horizontal line on the screen.
Observe the output of the sine wave oscillator (HP 200AB or CD) with
f = 20kc/s.

Now connect terminals 1 and 2 of the phase shift network to the oscillator.

Does the amplitude of the oscillator output voltage change when the
network is connected? _____ (Look carefully) Explain why   (a)
or why not. _____   (b)

The scope should be warmed up by now. Before continuing, check the
scope to see that it is properly adjusted and calibrated.

132

(a) external horizontal input

(b) time base

1.65 The AC-DC-GND switches on the vertical amplifier can be used to select the AC input, the DC input, or to ground the input to the vertical amplifier.

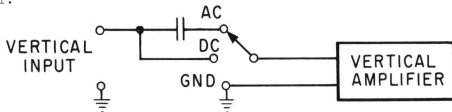

When set to AC, there is a blocking capacitor connected between the

_____ and the _____ (a,b)

When set to GND, the input to the vertical amplifier is

_____ volts. (c)

.5 sec/div

2.63 Observe the effect of rotating the red knob on the sweep rate. Rotating this knob counterclockwise _____ the speed at (a) which the spot moves across the screen.

The maximum time required for the spot to cross the screen (black knob still set to .5 sec/div) is _____. (b)

(a) 0.1 volts/div   (b) calibrated

If your observed deflection differs appreciably from 5 squares [4 squares for 561B], the gain needs adjustment. (503 ONLY: Ask your lab supervisor to check your scope if the deflection is less than 4.8 divisions or more than 5.2 divisions.)

3.66 Try to focus the trace as sharply as possible for several different settings of the intensity control. With the focus control set to an optimum position, what is the relation between the intensity and the thickness of the trace? _____

_____   (a)

Set the focus and intensity controls to what you think is an optimum position for making accurate measurements with the scope.

Now turn down the intensity slightly. If the trace is still clearly visible but you can focus for a finer, sharper trace, your original settings were probably not optimum.

Switch the +INPUT switch to AC and back to DC. Can either switch position be used for calibration? _____   (b)

If not, explain. _____   (c)

_____

(a) Yes.

(b) The oscillator is not an ideal voltage source, but it has an internal resistance. Therefore, the oscillator is "loaded down" by the network. In other words, the voltage drop across the internal resistance reduces the output voltage.

Did you check the DC BALANCE?

Did you check the calibration of the vertical amplifier by using the calibrator output?

[561: Did you also check the time base calibration?]

4.60 Before measuring the phase angle of v_2 with respect to v_1 using the triggered sweep method, it is necessary to calibrate the time axis in degrees. Indicate the proper connections to the scope for this calibration on the next page.

(a) vertical input   (b) vertical amplifier   (c) 0

1.66 503: The vertical amplifier is a differential amplifier.

561: The 2A63 plug-in is a differential amplifier.

This differential amplifier amplifies the difference of the +INPUT (v_+) and the -INPUT (v_-) so that the y-deflection is

$$y = (v_+ - v_-)/S_v$$

where S_v is the vertical sensitivity in volts/div. In this part, we will use only the +INPUT, so ground the -INPUT by using the AC-DC-GND switch above it. With the -INPUT grounded,

$$v_- = \rule{3cm}{0.4pt}$$ (a)

and the vertical deflection is given by

$$y = \rule{3cm}{0.4pt}$$ (b)

Throughout the rest of this part, leave the -INPUT grounded. The +INPUT is then equivalent to the vertical input, v_v.

503: The horizontal amplifier is also a differential amplifier. Ground both the +INPUT and the -INPUT on the horizontal amplifier.

(a) decreases

(b) approximately 15 sec (with the red knob fully counterclockwise)

2.64 Again with the sweep rate calibrated, observe the effect of changing the sweep rate. Observe that

    (a) at slow sweep rates the spot can be seen moving across the screen

    (b) as TIME/DIV is decreased the spot gradually becomes a line, but the line flickers on and off

    (c) as TIME/DIV is further decreased, the trace becomes a steady line without any noticeable flicker

What is the setting of the TIME/DIV switch at the boundary between condition (b) and condition (c)? $\rule{5cm}{0.4pt}$

(a) the greater the intensity, the thicker the trace
(b) no; only DC [yes for 561B]
(c) only DC can be used since the waveform is distorted in AC (the distortion is due to the blocking capacitor)

3.67

561 ONLY

The gain is adjustable by means of a screwdriver adjustment. Investigate the effect of this adjustment and then set it for exactly 5 divisions deflection [4 div for 561B]. (Use the position control as required to facilitate this adjustment).

Calibration could also have been done by setting the gain to 0.5 volt/div [0.2 for 561B] and adjusting for one square [2 squares for 561B] peak-to-peak deflection. Why would this be less desirable than using 5 [or 4] squares deflection as above? _____

_____ (a)

503 ONLY

When the 5 mv calibrator output is used, the deflection will be a whole number of divisions for sensitivity settings of _____ and _____. (b)

Observed deflections: _____ and _____, respectively. (c)

(If the trace goes off the screen when you attempt to observe the 5 mv calibrator output, what control needs adjustment?)

4.60 continued

Why should the network be connected to the source during this calibration?

_____ (b)

(a) $v_- = 0$ (b) $y = v_+ / S_v$ (i.e., the vertical deflection is directly proportional to the +INPUT voltage)

1.67   Set up the scope as follows:

1. Temporarily ground the vertical input with the AC-DC-GND switch.

2. Set the Volts/Div (sensitivity) switch to 1 volt (not 1 mVolt).

3. Turn up the INTENSITY control, adjust the two POSITION controls to obtain a centered spot on the screen.

WARNING: WHEN WORKING WITH A STATIONARY SPOT, USE A VERY LOW LEVEL OF INTENSITY

4. Adjust the INTENSITY so that the spot is clearly visible, but it is not any brighter than necessary. If the screen glows around the spot, it is too bright.

561
ONLY   { 5. If the AC Stabilized switch in the differential amplifier is ON, turn it OFF.

---

roughly   2 msec/div

2.65   Omit this frame if you have a Type 67 Time Base. This frame applies only to the Type 2B67 Time Base.

561
ONLY   With TIME/DIV set to .5 sec, move the mode switch to RESET and release. This causes the spot to _____.

Investigate the effect of single sweep operation at other sweep rates and then return the switch to NORM (repetitive sweep).

(a) The accuracy would be less. (The per cent error in reading the scope trace would be larger even though the absolute error would be about the same.)

(b) 5 mv/cm and 1 mv/cm   (c) 1 cm and 5 cm

3.68

561 ONLY

If the screwdriver gain adjustment has been properly set, the vertical amplifier calibration should be correct for all settings of VOLTS/DIV.

Check the calibration of the vertical amplifier on the 20 volt/div range. CALIBRATOR setting used: _____ (a)

Check the calibration of the vertical amplifier on the 10 mv/div range. CALIBRATOR setting used: _____ (b)

Was it necessary to readjust the screwdriver gain adj. in either case? _____ (c)

(a) Terminal 1 connected to +INPUT (vert.) and EXT. TRIG., terminal 2 to ground.

(b) Connecting the network loads down the oscillator and changes the voltage used for calibration.

4.61 Indicate the proper connections to the scope for measuring the phase angle of v_2 with respect to v_1 by the triggered sweep method.

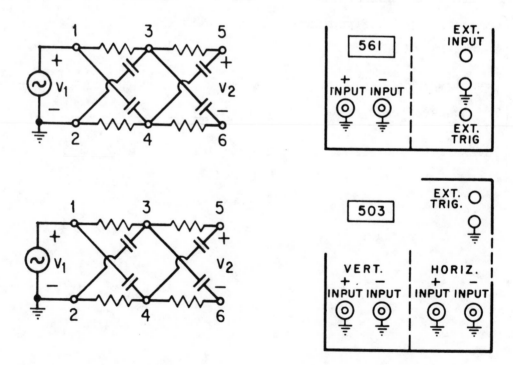

138

1.68 | Investigate the effect of operating the intensity and focus controls. Then adjust these controls to give a small sharp spot. If no spot is present on the screen, the _____ control should be (a) rotated _____. If the spot is fuzzy, the (b) _____ control should be adjusted. (c)

Note: If your scope has an ASTIGMATISM knob next to the FOCUS knob, it may be necessary to adjust the ASTIGMATISM in order to obtain a round spot. If a screwdriver slot is provided for ASTIGMATISM, no adjustment will usually be needed. In general, the ASTIGMATISM control is used in conjunction with FOCUS to obtain a uniform focus over the entire screen.

move across the screen once

2.66 | When the TRIGGERING LEVEL is not set to AUTO, a signal is required to trigger the sweep. This signal may come from the _____, the _____ or the _____. (a)

Set the SOURCE switch so that the sweep can be triggered from an external input.

Set the SLOPE to +, the COUPLING to DC, the LEVEL a little to the right of 0, and TIME/DIV to .2 sec.

Does the sweep trigger when there is no external trigger input?

_____ (b)

Momentarily apply a small positive DC voltage (about 10 volts) between the EXT. TRIG. input and ground. Describe what happens.

_____ (c)

If you have trouble getting the sweep to trigger, try adjusting the LEVEL. (561--Make sure you are using the EXT. TRIG. input, not the EXT. INPUT.)

(a) 100 volts [40 volts for 561B] should have been used (a smaller setting would be less accurate)

(b) 50 mv [40 mv for 561B]

(c) No. (If it was necessary, there may be something wrong with your scope. Ask the supervisor to check.)

3.69 When trying to make accurate voltage measurements with the scope, we should always use as large a deflection as possible because

_____ (a)

_____

Connect a sine-wave oscillator to the scope and set the output amplitude to about the middle of its range and observe the sine wave.

Leaving the red knob in the CALIBRATED position, rotate the VOLTS/DIV switch until the waveform <u>just</u> goes off scale (peak-to-peak deflection greater than 8 divisions); then back it down <u>one</u> position. The deflection should now be the maximum possible for the given input voltage.

observed peak-to-peak deflection _____ div. (b)

For three different input voltage amplitudes (different enough so you have to change ranges on the scope), record the maximum obtainable peak-to-peak deflection (VOLTS/DIV still calibrated):

_____ div. _____ div. _____ div. (c)

---

terminal 1 to EXT. TRIG., 2 to ground, 5 to +INPUT (vert.), 6 to -INPUT (vert.)

4.62 In preparation for measuring phase shift of the network, use a 1000 c/s sine wave source to calibrate the time axis for 20°/division with t = 0 at the left edge of the graticule. Do this as accurately as you can.

(a) intensity   (b) clockwise   (c) focus

1.69 Investigate the effect of operating the two position controls.

Rotating the vertical position control clockwise moves the spot

_____.   (a)

To move the spot to the right, rotate the _____   (b)

_____ control _____.   (c)

(a) vertical amplifier (internal trigger), AC line, external trigger
     input

(b) NO. (If your answer is YES, ask your supervisor to adjust the
     stability on the scope.)

(c) The spot crosses the screen once (since the sweep is triggered once).

2.67 Without changing the TIME/DIV, suppose you were to connect a sine
wave with a frequency of 0.2 c/s to the EXT TRIG input. Sketch the
sweep waveform (approximately) which should be generated by the TIME
BASE. (This waveform does not appear on the scope face, of course.)

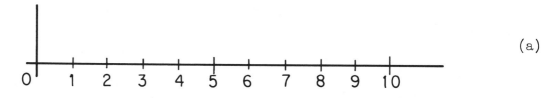
(a)

The sweep should be triggered once every _____ seconds and the   (b)

spot should take _____ seconds to cross the screen. Verify this   (c)

by observation. (If the sweep fails to trigger, turn up the amplitude

on the function generator.)

(a) the per cent error in reading the scope will be smaller when the deflection is large

(b,c) All of your answers should be in the range from 4 div. to 8 div. peak-to-peak regardless of the input voltage. If any of your answers are not in this range, go back and try three more different input voltages.

| 3.70 | Figs. 3-70x and y show the same sine wave displayed for two different settings of the position controls. In which case can you read the peak-to-peak deflection most accurately? _____ (a)

Positive peak on centerline

Negative peak on graticule line

FIG. 3-70x   FIG. 3-70y

Adjust the oscillator output voltage to 3.25 volts peak-to-peak. Do this as accurately as you can.

peak-to-peak deflection _____ div. (b)

Place a check after each of the following items which you did correctly:

(a) Network connected to source? ☐   (b) trigger SOURCE set to EXTernal ☐

(c) v_1 connected to both +INPUT and EXT. TRIG. ☐

(d) fine, sharply focused trace ☐

(e) peak amplitude 3 or more divisions ☐

(f) TIME/DIV (both black and red) set so that trace crosses axis at 9th division ☐

(g) horiz. position set so t = 0 here ☐

(h) trigger level set so trace starts here ☐

(i) if the vertical input is grounded (with the AC-DC-GND switch), the trace is centered ☐

If you missed any of these points, go back to frame 4.62 and try again.

TURN TO FRAME 4.63

(a) up   (b) horizontal position   (c) clockwise

1.70 The vertical sensitivity is adjustable by means of the black knob
labeled VOLTS/DIV (VOLTS/CM) and the red VARIABLE knob in the center.
Examine the sensitivity (VOLTS/DIV) control and note that one part
of the scale is labeled VOLTS (VOLTS/CM) and the other part is
labeled mVOLTS (mV/CM) (millivolts per centimeter). What vertical
input voltage would be required to produce a full scale deflection
of 4 cm if this control were set to its most sensitive position?

_____   (a)

If it were set to the least sensitive position?_____   (b)

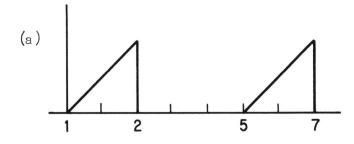

(a)

(b) 5 sec (once every cycle)
(c) 2 sec (.2 sec/div x 10 div)

2.68 Make the necessary changes so that the sweep will trigger 10 times a
second and the spot will take 50 ms to cross the screen. Record the dial
settings that you had to change. _____

_____

3.71 | Leave the oscillator set as in the preceding
frame. Connect the DC power supply in series
with the oscillator as shown. Set the DC
supply to 30 volts and observe v_1 using the
DC scope input. (If you have trouble getting
the sweep to trigger, use AUTO trigger.)
Could you measure the AC component of v_1
accurately when the scope is set to DC?

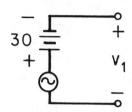

_____ Explain.

_____ (a)

Set the scope to measure the AC component of v_1 as accurately as
possible.

observed peak-to-peak deflection _____ (b)

The DC component of a waveform can be determined by observing the
amount of shift when the scope input is switched from AC to DC.
Measure the DC component of v_1 as accurately as you can by this
method.

number of divisions shift _____ (c)

DC component of v_1 _____ (include the sign) (d)

4.63 | Now measure the phase angle of v_2 with respect to v_1 at 1000 c/s.

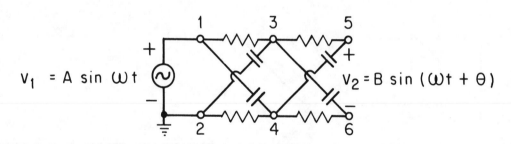

θ = _____

(a) 1 mv/div x 4 div = 4 mv (millivolts)

(b) 20 volt/div x 4 div = 80 volts

1.71 The voltage gain is calibrated only when the red knob is in the CALIBRATED position. A definite click will be heard and felt when going from cali- brated to uncalibrated and back. (Try it and see.) The numerical values of VOLTS/DIV printed on the scope apply only when the red knob is in the CALIBRATED position. If the scope is to be used for making accurate voltage measurements, the red knob that is concentric to the VOLTS/DIV knob should be rotated fully _____.

generator frequency changed to 10 c/s and TIME/DIV changed to 5 ms.

2.69 We have been triggering the sweep from an external source. Now set the TRIGGER SOURCE so the sweep will trigger from the vertical input.

Does the sweep trigger when there is no vertical signal present?
_____ (a)

If we want a sweep when there is no signal present, the LEVEL control should be set to _____ (b)

If all inputs are disconnected from the scope and the LEVEL control is set to 0, how should the SOURCE switch be set if we want the sweep to trigger? _____ (c)

Verify (b) and (c) by observation.

(a) No. The peak-to-peak deflection is too small.

(b) 6.5 div

(c) about 6 div (with S_v = 5 volts/div) (If you measured 3 div or less, go back and try for better accuracy. Use the position control if necessary.)

(d) Any answer in the range -28 to -32 volts is acceptable. It would be surprising if you measured exactly -30 volts since there are errors inherent in the meter as well as in the scope.

3.72 Skip this frame if you have a 561B.

561 ONLY

Since the screwdriver gain adjustment has been correctly set, do not change it. Using the calibrator output, adjust the VOLTS/DIV knobs (both black and red) so the vertical sensitivity is 2.5 volts/div. Do this as accurately as you can.

calibrator setting used   _____ (a)

volts/div setting   _____ (b)

peak-to-peak deflection   _____ (c)

503 ONLY

Check the calibration of the horizontal amplifier using the 500 mv calibrator output.

setting of horizontal display switch _____ (d)

observed peak-to-peak horizontal deflection _____ div. (e)

$\theta = -132°$ (any answer in the range -128° to -136° is acceptable)

If your answer checks within the prescribed tolerance, skip the rest of this frame.

4.64 If your answer is wrong, check the following:

(a) The triggering controls should be set exactly as they were in frame 4.62.

(b) The network should be connected as in frame 4.61.

(c) Both of the vertical input switches should be in the AC position (or both in the DC position).

(d) v_2 is negative at t = 0, so the sign of θ is _____.

(e) The magnitude of θ is _____ div x _____ degrees/div.

If you still can't get -132° ($\pm 4°$), your oscillator may need calibration.

Ask the supervisor for help.

146

clockwise (past the click stop, so that it is in the calibrated position)

1.72 Examine the vertical input connector on the scope.

The ungrounded or "high" side of the input should be connected to the
(center, outer) _____ conductor.   (a)

For this part, use a coaxial cable with clips on one end.

Connect this cable to the vertical input. Which of the coaxial cable
conductors is now grounded? (center, outer) _____.   (b)

The ungrounded conductor is terminated in a clip with a (red, black)
_____ insulator. (Use the continuity checker if you   (c)
can't tell by inspection.)

(a) no   (b) AUTO   (c) LINE

THIS IS A GOOD PLACE TO TAKE A BREAK

Displaying Periodic Waveforms

2.70 Set the vertical sensitivity to 10 volts/div and set the scope controls so that the vertical input will trigger the sweep.

If a 0.2 c/s sine wave were connected to the vertical input, the sweep
would be triggered once every _____ sec.   (a)

Verify your answer by observation. (Don't try to get a sine wave on
the screen; just observe the triggering of the sweep.) The input
and trigger coupling switches should both be set to _____
because _____.   (b)

(a) 20 volts   (b) 2 volts/div   (c) 8 div

(10 volts and 4 div could have been used, but this would be less accurate)

(d) Horiz. Amp. (sweep disabled)

(e) 5 (with S_h = 100 mv/div and the red knob in the calibrated position)

If the observed deflection differs more than 0.2 cm from 5 cm, ask the lab supervisor to check.

| 3.73 | 503 ONLY: TURN TO FRAME 3.78 |

503 ONLY: TURN TO FRAME 3.78

561 ONLY

Calibrating the Time Base (Type 2B67 or 67)

If the scope is to be used to make accurate time measurements, the TIME BASE must be properly calibrated.

For the 561 and 561A, the calibrator signal is the 60 c/s line frequency. [For the 561B, the calibrator signal is 1000 c/s.] If TIME/DIV is set to 5 msec [0.2 msec for 561B] and a calibrator signal is displayed, compute the number of cycles which should appear on the screen.

_____

Verify your answer by observation. (Check the red knob to make sure it is in the proper position.)

Record the value of θ which you measured at 1000 c/s in Table 4-1 (p. 201).

| 4.65 | When measuring phase shift by the triggered sweep method, the time axis of the scope must be recalibrated each time the frequency is changed because _____

_____ (a)

It is possible to go back and forth between phase measurement and calibration by moving only one lead and changing the position of only one slide switch. When changing from phase measurement to calibration, the lead connected to terminal _____ should be   (b)
moved to terminal _____ and the _____   (c,d)
switch should be set to _____.   (e)

(a) center   (b) outer   (c) red

THIS IS A GOOD PLACE TO TAKE A BREAK

Deflection of the Spot by DC Inputs

1.73 We are now ready to study the effects of applying DC signals to the scope input terminals.

Study Fig. A-1 (p. 221) which explains the functions of the controls on a typical low-voltage DC power supply. Note particularly that the ground terminal is a case ground and is <u>not</u> connected to either the + or - output terminal.

The equivalent circuit for the power supply output is:

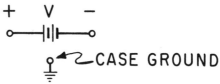

If the amplitude control on the power supply is adjusted so that the meter reads 4 volts, what voltage would you expect to measure

between the + terminal and ground?_____ (a)

between the - terminal and ground?_____ (b)

(a) once every 5 seconds (with TIME/DIV set to 0.2 sec or less)

(b) DC because the input is very low frequency

2.71 We now wish to display a 1000 c/s sine wave on the scope.

If we want to see exactly one cycle of the wave on the scope, we

should set the TIME/DIV to _____. (a)

If we set the TIME/DIV to .2 msec, what would you expect to see on

the screen? _____ (b)

Verify your answers experimentally. Set TRIGGER COUPLING to AC (AC SLOW for 561). It may be necessary to adjust the oscillator frequency <u>slightly</u> to get exactly one cycle on the screen for (a).

561,561A: $\dfrac{.005 \text{ sec/div} \times 10 \text{ div}}{1/60 \text{ sec}} = 3$ cycles   (since calibrator period is 1/60 sec)

561B: $\dfrac{.2 \text{ ms/div} \times 10 \text{ div}}{1 \text{ ms}} = 2$ cycles   (since calibrator period is 1/1000 sec)

If your observation differs appreciably from 3 cycles [2 cycles for 561B], the time base needs calibration.

3.74

561 ONLY

Investigate the effect of turning the screwdriver CALIBRATION adjustment on the TIME BASE, and then set this adjustment so that the TIME BASE is properly calibrated.

If the screwdriver calibration adjustment has been properly set, the time base calibration should be correct for all settings of TIME/DIV. How many cycles of the calibrator waveform should be observed for a setting of 10 ms/div [0.5 ms/div for 561B] _____

Verify this.

(a) Changing frequency changes the number of degrees per division

(b,c) 5, 1

(d,e) -INPUT, ground

4.66 Make sure your circuit is set up so that you have to move only one lead when switching between calibration and measurement.

Check the vertical centering of the trace with the input switches grounded to make sure that the trace hasn't drifted.

Now measure the phase shift at 100 c/s. $\theta = $ _____

If your answer to (a) is +4, continue with this frame; otherwise, turn to
the next frame.

1.74 The equivalent circuit for the power supply is:

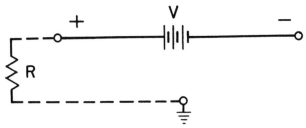

If we connect a resistor between + and ground as shown, how much current

will flow? _____ (The answer is _not_ V/R.) If we

replace the resistor with a voltmeter with internal resistance R, how

much current will flow? _____ If no current is flow-

ing in the meter, it will read _____. Now turn back to

frame 1.73 and try again.

(a) 0.1 msec/div (since period of sine wave is 1 msec)
(b) 2 cycles of the sine wave (since the spot takes twice as long to
     sweep across the screen)

2.72 (a) With the trace centered on the screen, adjust the TRIGGER LEVEL con-
           trol so that the sweep triggers _exactly_ when the sine wave goes
           through 0. Do this by observing the trace as you adjust the LEVEL;
           the 0 mark on the LEVEL control is not exact.

      (b) Without changing the LEVEL control, investigate the effect of changing
           the TRIGGER SLOPE SWITCH from + to -.

      (c) With the controls still set for 2 cycles of a 1000 c/s sine wave,
           sketch the waveform which you observe with the _slope_ set to -
           (negative).

      (d) Label the time scale.

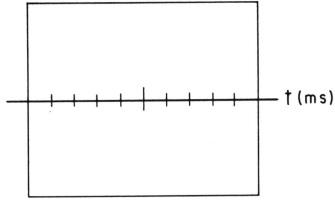

6 cycles [5 cycles for 561B]

3.75 | Using the calibrator output, adjust the TIME/DIV knobs (both red
and black) so that the sweep rate is 2.5 ms/div [.5 ms/div for 561B].
561
ONLY | Do not change the screwdriver adjustment.

setting of TIME/DIV _____ (a)

number of cycles on screen _____ (b)

-17° (an answer in the range -14° to -20° is acceptable)

If you didn't get the correct answer, try again.

When you get a value in the correct range, record it in Table 4-1 (p. 201).

4.67 | Now measure the phase shift at 300 c/s, 3000 c/s and at 10,000 cycles/
sec.

θ at 300 c/s = _____ (a)

θ at 3000 c/s = _____ (b)

θ at 10,000 c/s = _____ (c)

Answers to 1.73:

(a) 0 volts   (b) 0 volts (since neither the + or - terminal is
                        connected to ground)

1.75 Set the vertical sensitivity to 1 VOLT/DIV (calibrated).

Recenter the spot if necessary.

Connect a small positive DC voltage from the power supply to the vertical
input (+INPUT).

Set the AC-DC-GND switch to the proper position and observe the deflection
of the spot as the input voltage is varied.

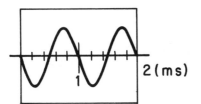

(If you didn't get this picture, go
back and try again. Make sure the
frequency is 1000 c/s.)

2.73 If you changed the signal generator to give a square wave of the same amplitude and frequency, sketch what you would expect to see on the scope.
(TRIGGER SLOPE still -)

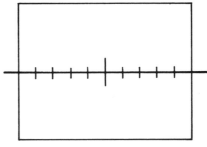

Make the change and check your prediction. Also investigate the effect of
changing the TRIGGER SLOPE when observing the square wave.

You should have set the black knob to 2 <u>msec</u> [.1 msec for 561B] and adjusted the red knob to obtain exactly <u>1-1/2 cycles</u> on the screen.

3.76

561 ONLY

The calibration of the TIME BASE should always be checked before attempting to make accurate time measurements. Since no two scopes are exactly alike, a plug-in must be recalibrated whenever it is moved from one scope to another.

To remove a plug-in from the scope, turn the aluminum knob at the bottom center of the plug-in several turns counterclockwise and pull. To insert a plug-in, push it all of the way into the opening and turn the knob clockwise until it is tight.

Trade horizontal plug-ins with another scope, and check the calibration of the new TIME BASE. Is it properly calibrated for your scope?

_____ (a)

Recalibrate the TIME BASE. TIME/DIV used _____ (b)

No. of cycles on screen _____ (c)

(a)   -48 $\pm$ 3° at 300 c/s
(b)   +125 $\pm$ 3° at 3 kc/s   (c)   +45 $\pm$ 3° at 10 kc/s

If correct, record your answers in the table.

If not correct, try again. Did you unground the -INPUT after calibrating?

Is the trace centered when both vertical inputs are grounded?

THIS IS A GOOD PLACE TO TAKE A BREAK

TURN TO FRAME 4.68

In this frame and many of the following frames, you will be asked
to predict a pattern or an input voltage <u>before</u> you check your
answer experimentally. Answer the questions and write down your
answers first. Wait to verify your answer experimentally until you
are told to do so.

An input voltage of +3 volts should deflect the spot upward
_____ divisions.   (a)

With the same input voltage, if the input switch is changed to AC,
the deflection should be _____.   (b)

After writing your answers, verify them experimentally.
Observed deflection, switch set to DC _____.   (c)
Observed deflection, switch set to AC _____.   (d)

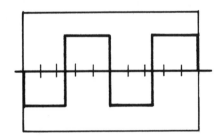

Change the input to a 800 c/s sine wave and observe the effect of
varying both the black TIME/DIV control and the associated red
VARIABLE control over a wide range of sweep rates. Now set the scope
to obtain the following picture:

Observed setting of TIME/DIV _____   (a)

Calibrated or uncalibrated? _____   (b)

Rotating the red VARIABLE control counterclockwise (increases/
decreases) _____ the time/div.   (c)

155

(a) Probably not, since there is quite a bit of variation from scope to
     scope.
(b and c) 561, 561A: 5 ms and 3 cycles (or 10 ms and 6 cycles, etc.)
     561B: 0.2 ms and 2 cycles (or 0.5 ms and 5 cycles, etc.)
If you forgot to set the red knob to the calibrated position, go back and
recalibrate.

3.77   Skip this frame if you have a 561B scope.

561
ONLY

Set the VOLTS/DIV to 2 mv (calibrated) and observe 6 cycles of the 10 mv
calibrator waveform on the screen. Observe the calibrator waveform under
each of the following conditions:

   (a) +INPUT set to AC, AC STABILIZED ON
   (b) +INPUT set to AC, AC STABILIZED OFF
   (c) +INPUT set to DC, AC STABILIZED ON
   (d) +INPUT set to DC, AC STABILIZED OFF

In which case(s) is it an undistorted square wave? _____

Why should AC STABILIZED be OFF when observing low frequency wave forms?

Phase Measurement by the Ellipse Method

4.68   When using the ellipse method, instead of displaying v_1 vs time or v_2 vs
time on the screen, we display v_2 vs v_1. Indicate the proper connections
to the scope for making phase measurements by the ellipse method.

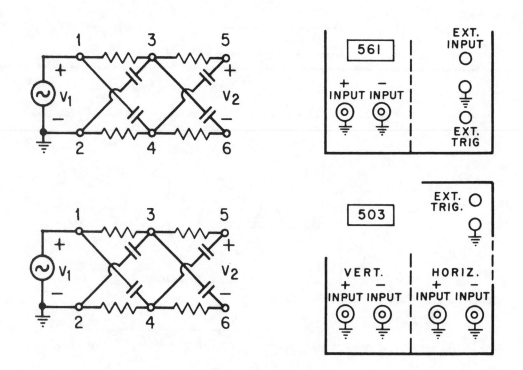

(a) 3   (b) 0

If your experimental answer doesn't check, ask your instructor to check
the calibration of your scope.

1.77 Full-scale vertical deflection (from center to the top grid line)

is _____ div.   (a)

Investigate the effect of the red gain knob (concentric to VOLTS/DIV)
on the deflection. When the red knob is fully counterclockwise,

_____ volts are required for a full-scale deflection,   (b)

so the sensitivity is _____ volts/div.   (c)

(a) .2 ms   (b) uncalibrated   (c) increases

2.75 Display several cycles of a 1000 c/s square wave on the screen. We
now want to adjust the amplitude of the signal generator output to
obtain a 12 volt peak-to-peak (6 volt peak) square wave.

What setting of VOLTS/DIV (vertical sensitivity) should be used?

_____   (a)

What should the peak-to-peak deflection be? _____   (b)

Now adjust the generator amplitude control to obtain a 12 volt
peak-to-peak output. (The amplitude control is not marked in volts,
so adjust it while watching the scope.)

(d) only

Turning on AC STABILIZED distorts low frequency waveforms.

3.78 Set the oscillator dial to 1500 c/s.

If the oscillator output frequency was exactly the same as the dial
setting, the period of the sine wave would be _____. (a)

Now measure the actual period of the sine wave as accurately as you
can. Choose an appropriate setting for TIME/DIV and adjust the
trigger controls to facilitate this measurement.

      Measured period _____ (b)

      TIME/DIV setting _____ (c)

---

v_1+ to EXT. INPUT (561) or horiz. +INPUT (503) v_1- to scope ground

v_2+ to vert. +INPUT v_2- to vert. -INPUT

4.69 1. Set up the scope to measure the phase shift of the network by the el-
    lipse method. Use the same phase shift network and oscillator that
    you used for the triggered sweep method. Do NOT use the Webb mask
    until you are told to do so.

  2. Set the vertical input switches to DC (also set the horiz. +INPUT to
    DC on the 503). Adjust the oscillator and scope controls to obtain an
    ellipse which occupies almost the entire height and width of the screen.

  3. Vary the oscillator frequency over its entire range and observe the
    effect on the ellipse.

    As the frequency approaches zero, the phase shift of the network
    approaches _____.

    At what frequency is the phase shift 180°? _____

(a) 4 div.   (b) about 10 to 20 volts

(c) to get sensitivity, divide your answer to (b) by 4.

1.78 Change the vertical gain to 5 volts/div (calibrated). Check the cen-

tering of the spot with the <u>input grounded</u> whenever you change the

gain setting. A vertical deflection of 2 divisions should require

an input of _____. Verify your answer experimental-   (a)

ly. Observed voltage _____.   (b)

(a) 2 volt/div (calibrated)   (b) 6 div.

2.76 Adjust the generator output to obtain a 3.5 volt peak-to-peak sine wave:

(a) First do this using 2 VOLTS/DIV as above.

(b) Change VOLTS/DIV to get the largest vertical deflection possible
and still have the peaks of the sine wave within the graticule.
(The red knob must remain in the CALIBRATED position of course.)
Now readjust the generator output if necessary to obtain 3.5 volts
peak-to-peak.

VOLTS/DIV setting _____ peak-to-peak deflection

_____.

(c) In which case, (a) or (b), was accurate adjustment of the sine
wave amplitude easier to make? _____

(d) In general, if we are trying to adjust the vertical input voltage
as accurately as possible, we should

_____

_____

(a) 1/1500 = 0.667 ms

(b) Any answer in the range 0.64 to 0.71 is acceptable (this allows for possible errors in the oscillator dial calibration and for errors in the scope sweep rate).

(c) 0.1 ms/div for one cycle on the screen (Or you could have set TIME/DIV for 2 or 3 cycles on the screen, measured the time for 2 or 3 periods of the sine wave and divided by 2 or 3.)

THIS IS A GOOD PLACE TO TAKE A BREAK

Use of the Probe

3.79 To reduce loading of the circuit, the probe should be used for making measurements on high-impedance circuits and for observation of high-frequency signals.

Recall the equivalent circuit of the probe and scope input:

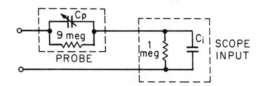

In order to compensate the probe so that the probe attenuation is independent of frequency and the probe will not distort waveforms, we must

---

O   1650 $\pm$ 50 c/s

If both of your answers are correct, turn to frame 4.71.

Otherwise, continue with this frame.

4.70 Check your circuit as follows:

Oscillator ground connected to scope ground? ☐

Other oscillator terminal (v_1+) connected to the external horizontal input? ☐

Output terminals from phase shift network (v_2) connected to +INPUT and -INPUT on vertical amplifier? ☐

Both input switches set to DC? ☐

[561 only: Oscillator output amplitude set to give desired trace width on screen? ☐]

Now turn back to frame 4.69 and try again.

(a) 10 volts   (b) 10 volts

1.79 | Change vertical gain to 0.5 volts/div.

An input of 2 volts should now deflect the spot _____   (a)
divisions.

Verify your answer experimentally. Observed deflection

_____.   (b)

Now turn the red VOLTS/DIV knob back and forth. As the red knob is
turned counterclockwise, the deflection of the spot _____   (c)
so the effective VOLTS/DIV _____.   (d)

(b) .5 volts/div, 7 div. (If you used 3.5 div, go back and try again.)
(c) accurate adjustment is easier in (b)
(d) use the largest possible vertical deflection

2.77 | Compute the TIME/DIV switch setting required to display 2 cycles of a
400 c/s triangular wave. _____   (a)
Verify your answer by observation.
With 2 cycles of a 400 c/s triangular wave displayed on the screen,
investigate the effect of adjusting the LEVEL control with the SLOPE
set to + and also with the SLOPE set to -.
Why does the trace disappear if the LEVEL control is turned too far
to either side of zero? _____   (b)
_____

adjust C_p (so that $C_p = C_1/9$)

3.80 Each time a probe is transferred from one scope to another, the compensation of the probe should be checked. If the calibrator output was observed using the probe and one of the waveforms of Fig. 5-8 (p. 217) was observed, in which case(s) must the compensation of the probe be adjusted?

_____

Record your answer to 4.69 in Table 4-1 (p. 201).

4.71 Before continuing with the phase measurements, we will examine a possible source of error in our measurements. In addition to amplifying the signal, the scope amplifiers may also introduce phase shift.

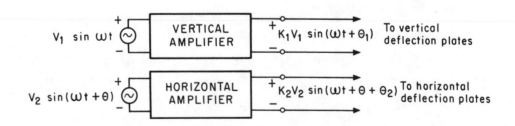

In the above diagram, the phase shift introduced by the vertical amplifier is _____ and that _introduced_ by horizontal (a)
amplifier is _____ (b)

What relation must hold between these angles if we want to introduce no error in the phase shift measurement by the ellipse method?

_____ (c)

162

(a) 4 div   (b) 4 div
(c) decreases   (d) increases

1.80 If the gain is set to 2 volts/div, then how many volts would be
required to deflect the spot <u>downward</u> 3 divisions?

_____   (a)

Verify your answer experimentally, still using the +INPUT on the
scope. (Make any necessary changes to the connections on the power
supply.) Observed voltage _____   (b)

(a) .5 ms/div   (b) The LEVEL is set above or below the peak of the
                        triggering signal, so the sweep does not trigger.

2.78 For each of the following waveforms, set the SLOPE and LEVEL so that the
trace begins at the leftmost graticule line with the slope and level shown.

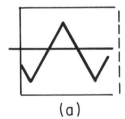
(a)

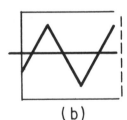
(b)

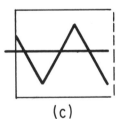
(c)

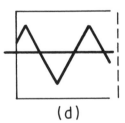
(d)

Record the SLOPE and LEVEL for each waveform:

	(a)	(b)	(c)	(d)
SLOPE				
LEVEL				

The compensation of the probe must be adjusted in cases (a) and (c) because the square wave is distorted.

3.81   Connect the probe cable to the vertical input.

Set TIME/DIV to 2 msec and, using the probe, display the 500 mv calibrator output [400 mv for 561B]. Set VOLTS/DIV for 5 div [4 div for 561B] peak-to-peak deflection. (Should the input be set to AC or DC? _____)

(a)

Study Fig. 3-81. (If your probe is of a different type than the one shown in the figure, ask the supervisor for instructions on how to loosen the locking sleeve and adjust the probe.)

Loosen the flanged locking sleeve on the probe several turns. Rotate the probe body and tip assembly while holding the base of the probe. CAUTION: Do not rotate more than two turns in either direction. As the probe is adjusted, observe how the displayed waveform gradually changes from Fig. 5-8 (a) to (b) to (c). What circuit element in the probe is being changed? _____

(b)

Adjust the probe for the correct waveform and then carefully tighten the locking sleeve.

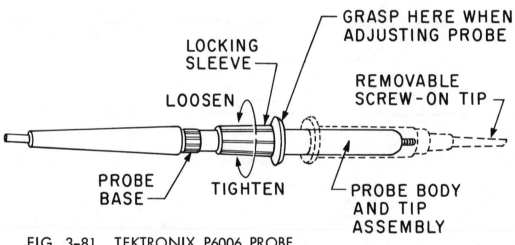

FIG. 3-81. TEKTRONIX P6006 PROBE

(a) θ_1 (b) θ_2 (c) $\theta_1 = \theta_2$

TURN TO FRAME 4.72

(a,b) -6 volts (Note that experimental verification requires reversing the connections to the DC supply so that the + terminal is grounded.)

1.81 If it is desired that an input voltage of 15 volts deflect the spot two divisions upward, the black VOLTS/DIV knob should be set to
_____ and the red knob should be set to the (calibrated, (a)
uncalibrated) _____ position. (b)

Verify your answers experimentally.
    Observed setting of black knob _____. (c)
    Observed setting of red knob _____. (d)

(slope) - + - +
(level) - - + +

2.79 Set the TRIGGER LEVEL to FREE RUN. Is the sweep now synchronized with the input signal? _____ (a)

For FREE RUN, is a sweep signal generated when there is no input?
_____ (b)

If the LEVEL is set to AUTO is the sweep synchronized with the input signal? _____ (c)

What is the difference between AUTO and FREE RUN?
_____ (d)
_____

(a) DC (AC setting will distort low-frequency waveforms)
     [For 561B, either AC or DC may be used since calibrator is 1000 c/s]

(b) Rotating the probe body changes the probe <u>capacitance</u>.

Recheck the compensation of the probe. Make sure that the corners of the
square wave are square with no rounding or overshoot.

3.82 Still using the probe to observe the 500 mv [400 mv] calibrator output and with the vertical deflection still 5 div [4 div] peak-to-peak,
the observed setting of the VOLTS/DIV switch is _____. (a)

When the probe is used, to get the true value of volts/div, the
setting of the VOLTS/DIV switch must be (multiplied/divided)

_____ by _____.   (b,c)

The probe attenuates the input signal by a factor of

_____.   (d)

4.72 How could you test to see if the phase shift produced by the **horizontal**
and vertical amplifiers is the same?

_____

_____

_____

_____

If you want a hint, turn to frame 4.73.
If you know the answer, turn to frame 4.74.

(a,c) 5 volts/div   (b,d) uncalibrated

1.82 | Examine the terminals on the TIME BASE. The ungrounded side of the
horizontal input should be connected to the (top, middle, bottom)

561
ONLY

_____ terminal and the grounded side to the   (a)

_____ terminal.   (b)

Apply a DC voltage to the horizontal input and observe the deflection
of the spot as the voltage is varied.

The horizontal sensitivity is fixed and cannot be varied on the 561 series scopes. Apply enough voltage for full-scale deflection of the
spot and determine this sensitivity. Measured voltage? _____ (c)

S_h = _____ volts/div   (d)

(a) No   (b) Yes   (c) Yes
(d) The sweep is synchronized with the input in AUTO but not in FREE RUN

2.80 | Up to this point you have been using the function generator as a signal
source. Now you will use a sine wave oscillator (HP 200AB or 200CD or
equivalent) instead. Examine the controls and terminals on your oscillator.
If it is type HP 200AB or 200CD it will have three terminals at the bottom
arranged as follows:

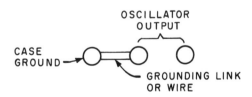

The left terminal is a case ground (which is connected to the building
ground if there is a 3-wire line cord). The sine-wave signal is taken from
the right two terminals. For normal operation, a grounding link or wire
is connected between the center terminal and the case ground as shown.

Observe the oscillator output for several different frequencies and for
several settings of the oscillator amplitude control.

(a) 10 mv   (b) multiplied   (c) 10   (d) 10

3.83   Next we will observe the loading effect of the scope without and then with the probe.

Connect the circuit shown below. Set the oscillator frequency to 100 c/s. Observe the oscillator output with the scope (use the coaxial cable lead, <u>not</u> the probe). Adjust the oscillator to obtain an output of V_1 = 10 volts peak-to-peak as accurately as you can. (Leave the network connected to the oscillator when you measure the oscillator output since the output may change when you disconnect the network.) What VOLTS/DIV setting did you use?

_____   (a)

How many divisions peak-to-peak deflection did you obtain?

_____ .   (b)

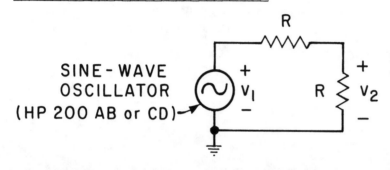

Use R ≈ 500 kilohms. Obtain a pair of precision resistors from the supervisor.

4.73   Hint:

If we connect the same signal to both the vertical and horizontal inputs, what should we see if the phase shift in the vertical and horizontal amplifiers is the same? _____

What should we see if the phase shift is slightly different?

_____

Now go back and answer frame 4.72.

(a) top   (b) middle

(c) approx. 3 to 10 volts are required for a full-scale deflection of
     5 div.

(d) divide the measured voltage by 5 to get the sensitivity

| 1.83 |

503
ONLY

Next we will observe the horizontal deflection of the spot. The
horizontal differential amplifier is identical to the vertical amplifier.

If we want the horizontal deflection to be proportional to the
applied voltage v_h, we should connect v_h to the horizontal (+INPUT,
-INPUT) _____ and ground the _____.   (a,b)
If the horizontal sensitivity is set to 2 volts/cm, the input voltage
required to produce a deflection of 4 cm is _____.   (c)
With the same input voltage, how could you get a deflection of 3 cm?
_____.   (d)

Verify your answers experimentally.

| 2.81 | Put a 200 c/s sine wave into the vertical input. Use AC (AC SLOW) trigger
coupling and adjust the scope controls to obtain the following picture.

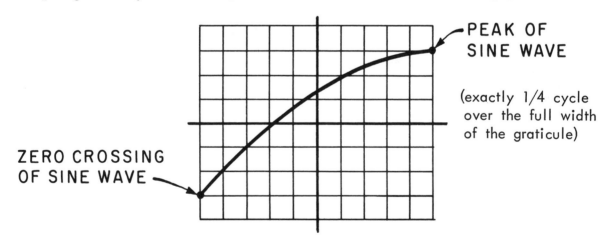

PEAK OF
SINE WAVE

(exactly 1/4 cycle
over the full width
of the graticule)

ZERO CROSSING
OF SINE WAVE

Suggestion: With one or two cycles of the sine wave on the screen, adjust
the vertical position and oscillator output to give the desired zero line
and peak deflection. Then adjust the TIME/DIV and triggering controls to
give the desired trace.

(a) 2 VOLTS/DIV   (b) 5 div.

You also could have used 5 volts/div and 2 div or 10 volts/div and 1 div,
but this would not be as accurate. If you didn't use 2 volts/div and
5 div, check your result using these values (adjust the position control
as required).

3.84 Still using the coax cable lead, measure the peak-to-peak value of
V_2. Explain why V_2 differs from the theoretical value of 5.

_____ (a)

Now measure V_2 for f = 1 kc/s, 10 kc/s and 40 kc/sec. Each time you
change frequency observe the oscillator output (V_1) to make sure that
it is still 10 volts peak-to-peak (with the network connected).

Complete the following table:

f(c/s)	V_1	V_2
100	10	
1K		
10K		
40K		

← peak-to-peak voltages

(b)

Explain why V_2 decreases with increasing frequency._____

_____ (c)

(If you can't explain it, go back and review frame 3.6.)

Answer to 4.72:
Connect the oscillator to both the vertical input and the horizontal input.
Phase shift is the same if the trace is a diagonal line (/).

4.74 Carry out the above procedure. Set the vertical amplifier to DC (also

the horizontal amplifier on the 503). Adjust the scope and oscillator

controls to obtain a trace which occupies nearly the full width and

height of the screen. Observe the phase shift error as the frequency

is varied from 20 c/s to 40 kc/s.

561
ONLY   Over what frequency range is the error negligible?

_____ to _____. At what frequency in the   (a)

range 20 c/s to 40 kc/s is the error maximum? _____   (b)

503   Is the error negligible over the entire range? _____   (c)
ONLY

170

(a) +INPUT   (b) -INPUT   (c) 8 volts

(d) set the red knob to the uncalibrated position and adjust it

---

1.84 By now you should know how to connect and adjust the scope to deflect the spot by any desired amount in either direction.

With the spot initially centered, connect the DC power supply to the appropriate input terminals and adjust the power supply and scope controls so that the spot is deflected to the position x = 1, y = 2. (Do not readjust the position controls once the spot is centered.)

Check your results as follows. Change the black TIME/DIV switch setting to twice its present value. You should now see the waveform shown at the right (with the peak in the center).

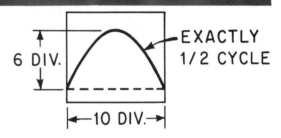

If you get this waveform, turn to the next frame.
If you failed to get the right waveform, turn back to frame 2.81 and try again. If you need help, continue with this frame.

2.82 Try using the following procedure:

(a) Ground the vertical inputs and obtain a horizontal line on the screen. Position this line to one division from the bottom of the grid.

(b) Observe one or two cycles of the 200 c/s sine wave and set the peak amplitude for 6 divisions above the zero line established in (a). (Adjust the VOLTS/DIV or oscillator output or both as required.)

(c) Check the position of the zero line as in step (a) and repeat steps (a) and (b) if necessary.

(d) Set the trigger source to INT, trigger coupling to AC (AC SLOW), trigger slope to +, and adjust the trigger level until the sweep triggers at the zero crossing of the sine wave.

(e) Position the zero point to the left edge of the grid if necessary.

(f) Set TIME/DIV (both black and red) to give exactly one quarter cycle on the screen.

(g) Repeat (e) and (f) if necessary. When you are satisfied that the scope picture is exactly as shown in frame 2.81, check your answer by the method described above.

(a) The input impedance of the scope loads down the circuit.

(b) V_2 = 4, 3.9, 1.8, 0.5. (If your answers don't check within $\pm$ .2 volts, try again. Each time you change the oscillator frequency, make sure that you readjust the oscillator output for 10 volts peak-to-peak.)

(c) The loading increases with increasing frequency due to the shunt capacitance.

3.85 Repeat the measurements made in frame 3.84 using the probe instead of the coaxial cable lead. What change should be made in the setting of VOLTS/DIV to compensate for the probe attenuation? _____ (a)

f(c/s)	V_1	V_2
100	10	
1K	10	
10K	10	
40K	10	

← peak-to-peak voltages

(b)

Compare with the results of 3.84 and <u>explain the difference</u>.

_____ (c)

_____

(a) 20 c/s to about 1 kc/s or 2 kc/s (This will vary from scope to scope but you should notice some phase shift error by the time you reach 5 kc/s)

(b) 40 kc

(c) Yes. (If it is not, your scope probably needs adjustment. Ask the supervisor.)

4.75 We can compensate for this phase shift error by adding some phase shift to the horizontal input. If a resistance is added in series with the horizontal input, phase shift will occur because of the shunt capacitance at the scope input.

Connect a 10,000 ohm potentiometer* in series with the horizontal input as shown. Connect the case ground on the pot to the scope ground. Adjust the pot so that there is no phase shift error at 40 kc/s.

561 ONLY

*Note the connections to the pot; a variable resistance is obtained between the center terminal and an end terminal.

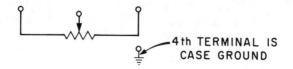

4th TERMINAL IS CASE GROUND

You should have connected the + terminal of the power supply to <u>both</u> the vertical and horizontal scope inputs. (If your x deflection isn't exactly 1 div, adjust the power supply voltage. Then if your y deflection isn't exactly 2 div, adjust the red VARIABLE knob on VOLTS/DIV.)

THIS IS A GOOD PLACE TO TAKE A BREAK

Scope Traces Due to Time-Varying Inputs

1.85 We will now study the effects of applying AC signals to the scope terminals. We will still be operating the scope with an external horizontal input connected to the horizontal amplifier (sweep disabled) so that there will be no horizontal deflection unless we apply a horizontal input voltage. Check to see that the scope is set so that there is a small dot in the center of the screen when no inputs are connected.

We will use a low frequency function generator (HP 202A or equivalent) as a signal source. Study the functions of the function generator operating controls as shown in Fig. A-2 (p. 222). When the vertical input of the scope is connected to the function generator, the red clip on the scope cable should be connected to terminal no. _____ (a) and the black clip to terminal no. _____. The scope ground and (b) function generator ground are connected together through the 3-wire line cords. Assuming that the grounding link is in place, what would happen if the red and black clips were interchanged? _____

_____. (c)

Set the AC-DC-GND switch on the vertical +INPUT to the appropriate position for observation of very low frequency signals. To what position did you set it? _____ (d)

TURN TO FRAME 2.83

(a) decrease by a factor of 10

(b) V_2 = 4.9, 4.9, 4.8, 3.8 (try again if your answers don't check within $\pm$ .2)

(c) The probe has a higher input impedance so it does not load the circuit as much.

THIS IS A GOOD PLACE TO TAKE A BREAK

Use of the Differential Amplifier

3.86 | Back in frame 3.60 you adjusted the DC BALANCE of the vertical amplifier. Check to see that the amplifier is still balanced, and readjust the DC BALANCE if necessary.

Until now, we have used only the +INPUT and we have not used the differential amplifier in the differential mode.

Connect the output of the sine-wave oscillator to both the +INPUT and -INPUT (in parallel). Use a frequency of 5 kc/s and set the oscillator output amplitude for 4 volts peak-to-peak. With the -INPUT grounded, adjust the scope so that 2 cycles of the sine wave cover the entire screen.

Now ground the +INPUT and unground the -INPUT. Is the picture now inverted? _____ (a)

Explain why or why not. _____

_____ (b)

If you can't explain it, turn to frame 3.87; otherwise go on to frame 3.88.

When the pot is properly adjusted, you should have a diagonal line on the screen.

4.76 | With the pot adjusted as above, check the phase error at all frequencies in the range 20 c/s to 40 kc/s. The error is _____ at all fre- (a)

561
ONLY | quencies in the range. For the rest of Part IV, leave the pot in series with the horizontal input.

ALL | At 20 c/s observe the effect of switching the _vertical_ amplifier input from DC to AC. Explain. _____

_____ (b)

561
ONLY | What is the minimum frequency at which the AC position can be used without causing any noticeable phase shift error? _____ (c)

503
ONLY | Now set both the vertical and horizontal inputs to AC and check the phase error at all frequencies in the range 20 c/s to 40 kc/s
Is the error still negligible over the entire range? _____ (d)

(a) 1   (b) 2 (or 3 if the grounding link is in place)

(c) the output would be shorted out through the scope ground

(d) If your answer is <u>AC</u>, continue with this frame; otherwise turn to the next page.

| 1.86 | When the switch is in the AC position, there is a blocking capacitor in series with the input as shown in frame 1.44. When the frequency of the input signal is very low, the impedance of the blocking capacitor $(1/\omega C)$ will be very _____, and the input voltage to the scope will be _____.

Now turn back to 1.85(d) and try again.

| 2.83 | By observation of the trace, adjust the scope to observe 5 cycles of a 250 c/s square wave. Now connect a sine-wave oscillator to the external <u>trigger</u> input (watch the grounds). Set the oscillator to 250 c/s and switch the trigger source to EXT. Turn up the oscillator amplitude about half way to assure that the triggering signal is adequate. Can a stable picture be obtained if the sine wave is not exactly the same frequency as the square wave? _____ (a)

Very carefully adjust the oscillator frequency to obtain a nearly stationary picture on the screen. Even with the most careful adjustment, the picture will gradually drift across the screen. What does this imply about the frequencies of the two oscillators?

_____ (b)

<u>Compute</u> two other sine-wave oscillator frequencies less than 250 c/s at which a stationary picture could be obtained. (The vertical input and scope controls remain the same as above.) Computed values:

_____ _____ (c)

3.87 | If the vertical input is as follows, where will the sweep trigger if the
SLOPE is set to + and the LEVEL to 0?   (indicate with an arrow)

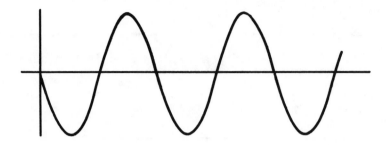

Now turn back to frame 3.86 and explain why the input doesn't appear
inverted.

(a) 0 or negligible   (b) In the AC position, the blocking capacitor
                             causes phase shift at low frequencies.

(c) about 200 to 500 c/s
(d) Yes

4.77 | Now reconnect the phase shift network.
At what frequencies is the phase shift +90° or -90°? _____,

_____

Can you tell which is which using the ellipse method only?

_____   (a)

Since the phase shift of the network varies smoothly as the frequency
varies, we can determine the sign of the phase shift from the triggered
sweep data previously taken. From Table 4-1, at frequencies less than
1600, the sign of the phase shift is _____ and at frequencies   (b)
greater than 1800 the sign is _____.   (c)
At what frequency is the phase shift +90? _____   (d)
                              -90? _____   (e)

Answer to 1.85(d): You should have set the switch to DC. (At very low frequencies, the AC position cannot be used because the impedance of the blocking condenser is too high.)

1.87 With no horizontal input, if a sine wave is applied to the vertical input, describe the expected motion of the spot at very low frequencies.

_____ (a)

What should be observed at high frequencies?

_____ (b)

After writing your answers, observe the above using the following procedure:

    (a) For this and the following frames use a vertical sensitivity of 1 volt/div and adjust the signal amplitudes as required for a reasonable deflection.

    (b) Connect the low frequency function generator to the vertical input. Use sine wave output and vary the frequency between about 0.1 and 100 c/s.

<hr>

(a) No.

(b) they are not exactly the same; they are not synchronized; they are not constant so that one is changing with respect to the other

(c) Verify your own answers experimentally. (Since the oscillator dial reading is not exact, a slight adjustment of the oscillator frequency will probably be necessary to get a stationary picture.)

2.84 (a) Now connect the _same_ sine-wave oscillator to both the vertical input and to the EXT. TRIGGER input. Set TRIGGER LEVEL to 0. Switch the trigger source back and forth between EXT. and INT. Notice that you get a stationary picture in either position since the triggering voltage comes from the same oscillator in either position.

(b) With trigger source set to EXT, increase the VOLTS/DIV until the sine wave goes to zero and only a horizontal line remains.

(c) Reset VOLTS/DIV to obtain the original sine wave again. Switch trigger source to INT and increase VOLTS/DIV. Observe that the whole trace disappears when the sine wave amplitude gets small.

(d) Explain why a horizontal line remains in (b) but the trace completely disappears in (c). _____

_____

_____

(If in doubt, study Fig. 5-3 on p. 211 again.)

(a) No.

(b) Even though the sign of the input is changed, the scope still triggers at the same point on the waveform.

3.88 Now set both the +INPUT and -INPUT to AC.

Set the trigger level so that you get a trace (even though the effective vertical input is 0).

If the amplifier were ideal, the deflection would be _____.   (a)

Adjust the VOLTS/DIV to obtain a deflection of about 2 div.*

The actual peak-to-peak deflection is _____ div. with   (b)

S_v = _____.   (c)

Since the input signal is 4 volts peak-to-peak for both v_+ and v_-,

the common-mode gain is K_c = _____ div/volt   (d)

The difference mode gain is $K_d = 1/S_v$ = _____   (e)

Therefore, the common-mode rejection ratio is CMRR = _____.   (f)

---

*If you can't get 2 div, use the largest deflection you can get.

(a) No.   (b) -   (c) +

(d) 4300 to 4800 c/s   (e) 570 to 630 c/s

If your answers don't check, try again. When you have obtained answers which are within the prescribed tolerance, record them in the table.

4.78 Still using the ellipse method, measure the phase shift at 1000 c/s.

Adjust the vertical deflection for about 8 divisions peak-to-peak to obtain maximum accuracy.

$|\theta|$ = _____

Determine the sign of θ from previous data.

θ = _____

(a) The spot will move up and down (at the sine wave frequency).

(b) The moving spot will become a vertical line. (If your answer was "a sine wave" you are wrong because there is no horizontal signal and hence no horizontal deflection.)

1.88 If the sine wave is changed to a triangular wave, should there be any appreciable change in the observed picture? _____ (a)

After writing your answer, observe this on the scope.

If the triangular wave is changed to a square wave, what should be observed at very low frequencies (assume that the square wave is ideal so that it jumps instantaneously between its maximum and minimum values)? _____

_____ (b)

At high frequencies? _____ (c)

After writing your answers, observe the above phenomena on the scope.

(d) In (b) the triggering voltage remains constant, but in (c) the triggering voltage decreases as the vertical amplifier output decreases.

2.85 Now disconnect the EXTernal trigger lead and use only the INTernal trigger for this part.

(a) With trigger level set to AUTO, obtain a sine wave on the screen. Gradually turn down the oscillator output until the sine wave goes to zero and only a horizontal line remains.

(b) Reset the oscillator output to obtain the original sine wave and set trigger LEVEL to 0. Now turn down the oscillator amplitude and observe that the whole trace disappears when the amplitude gets small.

(c) Explain why a horizontal line remains in (a) but the trace completely disappears in (b). _____

_____

_____

_____

Trigger level should be set to AUTO.

(a) 0   (b,c,e) Answer will vary from scope to scope.

(d) Divide answer to (b) by 4.

(f) Divide K_d by K_c. The result should be in the range 100 to 4000. If it is not, your scope may need adjustment. Ask the supervisor to check.

3.89 Now turn up the oscillator amplitude slowly. With VOLTS/DIV set to .2 or less at what input amplitude does distortion start to occur?

_____

(The input amplitude should be measured with the -INPUT grounded after distortion has been observed in the differential mode.)

Did you center the ellipse horizontally before reading the deflections? Your answer should check within 4° of the value measured by the triggered sweep method. If it doesn't, find out why before continuing. When you get a correct answer, record it in the table.

4.79 Carefully center the Webb mask over the graticule lines.

Adjust the trace so that with the vertical inputs grounded, the trace

lies along line _____ and with the horizontal input dis-   (a)

connected the trace lies along line _____.   (b)

Read θ from the Webb mask. $\theta =$ _____ or _____

Which of these values is correct? _____   (c)

(a) No. (except the spot will now travel up and down at a uniform rate)

(b) The dot will jump up and down (between the two positions which correspond to the maximum and minimum of the square wave).

(c) The dot will appear in both places simultaneously (because of persistence of the screen).

1.89 Now ground the vertical input.

[503 ONLY: Set the horizontal +INPUT switch to the appropriate position for very low frequency AC signals. Use 1 volt/cm sensitivity.]

If a sine wave is applied to the horizontal input, what should be observed at low frequencies? _____ (a)

at high frequencies? _____ (b)

After writing your answers, observe the above on the scope.

For AUTO trigger the sweep triggers even when no triggering signal is present. In (b) the trace disappears when the triggering signal becomes too small.

2.86 A 6 volt peak-to-peak, 1000 c/s sine wave is added to a 4 volt DC level to give

$$v(t) = 3 \sin 2000\pi t + 4$$

If $v(t)$ is observed with a scope set to 2 volts/div and AUTO trigger, sketch the expected waveform if (a) the vertical AC input is used and (b) the vertical DC input is used.

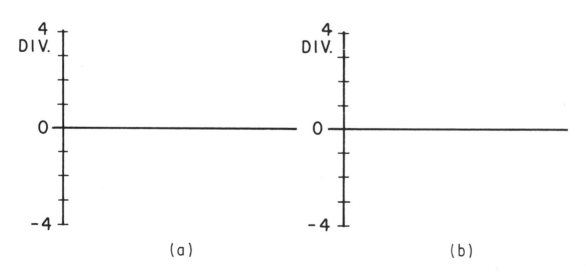

(a)　　　　　　　　　　　　　(b)

Your answer should be in the range 10 to 20 volts peak-to-peak (561) or 4 to 20 volts peak-to-peak (503).

3.90 The trace is centered with no inputs applied, and both inputs are then set to DC. If a 6 volt peak-to-peak (3 volts peak) sine wave is then applied between the +INPUT and ground, +4 volts DC is applied between the -INPUT and ground, and S_v is set to 2 volts/div, the vertical deflection should be

$$y = \underline{\hspace{5cm}}$$ (a)

Sketch the expected trace.

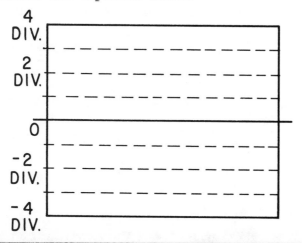

(b)

Verify your answer by observation.

(a) B - B'   (b) A - A'

(c) Again, your answer should check within 4° of the value measured by triggered sweep. Make sure your ellipse is tangent to all four sides of the square on the Webb mask.

4.80 Now measure the phase shift at 100, 300, 3000, and 10,000 c/s. In each case, first compute the angle from distances measured on the ellipse and **then** read the value from the Webb mask.

When the oscillator frequency is changed, is it necessary to make any other adjustments before reading the phase angle from the Webb mask?

$\underline{\hspace{3cm}}$ (a)

If so, what? $\underline{\hspace{8cm}}$

$\underline{\hspace{10cm}}$ (b)

Record the computed angles and the angles read from the Webb mask in Table 4-1. (The table should now be complete except for the shaded areas.)

(a) The spot will move back and forth at the sine wave frequency.

(b) The moving spot will become a horizontal line.

1.90 With the sine wave still applied to the horizontal input, what should be the effect of applying + 2 volts DC to the vertical input?

_____

After writing your answer, observe this on the scope.

Verify your answers experimentally using the procedure below.

2.87 Set the sine-wave oscillator to 6 volts peak-to-peak, and set the DC power supply to 4 volts. To add the DC voltage to the sine-wave voltage, you must connect the DC power supply in (series/parallel)

_____ with the oscillator. Indicate the proper   (a)
connections to the scope on the diagram below. Make sure that you
have a common ground wire between the oscillator and scope and that the
power supply polarity is correct.

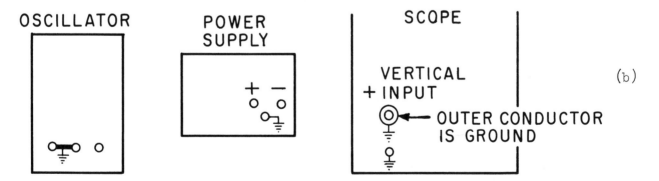

OSCILLATOR   POWER   SCOPE
                  SUPPLY

                                 VERTICAL   (b)
                                 + INPUT
                                          ← OUTER CONDUCTOR
                                            IS GROUND

Connect the circuit and verify your answers to the preceding frame.
Make sure the trace is centered when the scope input is grounded.
When the input switch is changed from DC to AC, the trace moves

(up/down) _____   _____ div.   (c)

(a) 1/2 (3 sin ωt -4) =
         1.5 sin ωt - 2

If your prediction and observation
don't agree, go back and try again.
Note that the deflection should be
-2 div if you ground the +INPUT.

(b)

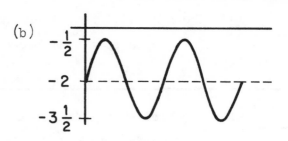

3.91 | Measure the common-mode gain and compute the common-mode rejection
ratio using a 40 kc/s sine wave input with 4 volts peak-to-peak amplitude. Note that the common-mode rejection ratio varies with the
setting of VOLTS/DIV.

K_c = _____   (a)

CMMR = _____   (b)

measured with S_V = _____   (c)

(a) yes
(b) Adjust oscillator output and/or oscilloscope sensitivity so ellipse
     is tangent to all four sides of the square. (This is most easily
     accomplished by grounding one input at a time as in frame 4.79a and b.)
(c) Computed angles should agree with values from Webb mask within 3°.

4.81 | Now measure the phase shift of V_2 with respect to V_1 at 3000 c/s when the
network is connected as follows:

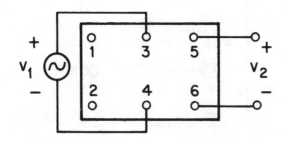

θ (calculated from ellipse) =
$\sin^{-1}$ _____ = _____   (a)

θ (read from Webb mask) =

_____   (b)

Check your answers by the triggered sweep method.

θ (by triggered sweep) =

_____   (c)

The trace will move up 2 divisions.

1.91 What should be observed if the same sine wave is applied to both
      horizontal and vertical inputs? _____

      After writing your answer, observe this on the scope.

(a) series   (b) right terminal of oscillator to power supply -,
                    + terminal of power supply to center of scope vertical
                    input

(c) down 2

Answers to 2.85: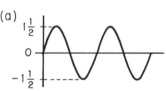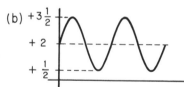

If your observed waveforms are not the same as above, go back and try again.

2.88 With the same input as in 2.86, vertical input set to DC, triggering
      LEVEL set to 0 or slightly -, determine the following:

      (a) Will the sweep trigger if DC trigger COUPLING is used?

           _____   (a)

      (b) Will the sweep trigger if AC (AC SLOW for 561) trigger
           COUPLING is used? _____   (b)

      Explain the difference:

      _____

      _____   (c)

You should have set the oscillator output to 4 volts peak-to-peak (with the -INPUT grounded). Then with the oscillator connected to both +INPUT and -INPUT, you should have set S_v for an adequate deflection. If this deflection is y_1 (peak-to-peak), then $K_c = y_1/4$, $K_d = 1/S_v$, and CMRR = K_d/K_c. CMRR should be greater than 100.

3.92 This exercise will test your ability to operate the scope.

(a) Rotate the following controls fully counterclockwise: focus, intensity, vert. position, horiz. position, calibrator, VOLTS/DIV and variable, TIME/DIV and variable. Rotate DC BALANCE about a turn clockwise. Place all slide switches in the lowest position.
561 ONLY: Uncalibrate both plug-ins with a screwdriver.

Keep a record of the time required to do parts (b) and (c)

(b) Adjust the DC BALANCE.
561 ONLY: calibrate both plug-ins.
503 ONLY: check calibration of the vert. amp.
Check the probe and adjust it if necessary.

(c) Using the probe, display 3 cycles of a 2 volt peak-to-peak 400 c/s sine wave on the scope with the waveform starting at this point ———

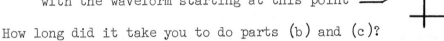

How long did it take you to do parts (b) and (c)?

_____

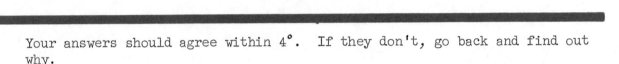

Your answers should agree within 4°. If they don't, go back and find out why.

4.82 If you vary the frequency continuously and observe the ellipse, how can you tell when the phase angle goes through 0° or 180°?

_____ (a)

The phase shift of most networks is a smooth function of frequency; therefore, when the phase angle passes through zero degrees, a plot of phase angle vs frequency will look like

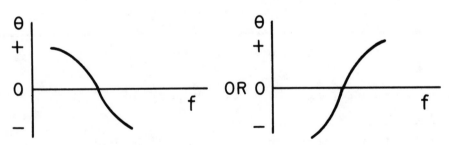

By watching the ellipse, how can you tell when the phase angle changes sign as the frequency is varied?

_____ (b)

186

a diagonal line (since the vertical and horizontal deflections are about equal)

$\boxed{1.92}$ For the following circuit, if $v_h = V_h \sin \omega t$, then $v_v \approx V_h/\omega RC \cos \omega t$ as was derived in the preparation. What should be observed on the scope? _____

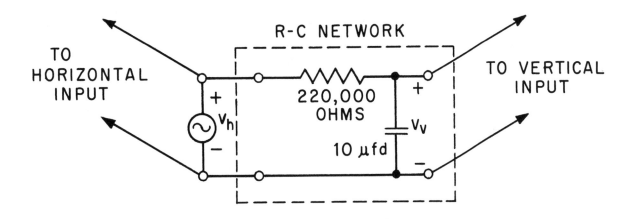

R-C NETWORK

TO HORIZONTAL INPUT

v_h 220,000 OHMS 10 μfd v_v

TO VERTICAL INPUT

(a) no   (b) yes

(c) For DC coupling, the entire signal is used for the trigger input, and since this signal never goes to 0 or negative, triggering never occurs. For AC coupling, only the AC component is used so the trigger circuit input does go through 0 and triggering occurs.

$\boxed{2.89}$ With AC trigger coupling, adjust the DC power supply and the scope controls to obtain the following picture:

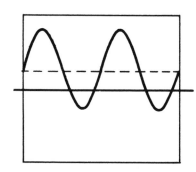
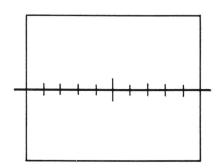

Draw an arrow on the waveform above to indicate where the sweep will trigger when the trigger coupling is changed to DC (with trigger level and slope unchanged). Then sketch the waveform you would expect to see if the trigger coupling is changed to DC. Verify your answer by observation.

Hum and Noise Pickup

3.93 The leads which connect the scope (or other measuring instrument) to the signal being observed may pick up extraneous signals. Such extraneous signals may cause fuzzy pictures on the screen and make accurate measurements impossible. In this section we will observe some of the conditions under which extraneous signals can be picked up, and we will investigate some things which can be done to eliminate them.

Attach an unshielded long lead (about 30" long) to the +INPUT of the vertical amplifier and set TIME/DIV to 5 ms. Leave the lead stretched out on the bench with the other end not connected. Adjust the scope to obtain a good picture. What is the frequency of the signal which is picked up by the lead? _____ (a)

Observe that the trace will sync on LINE trigger as well as INT trigger.

What do you think is the source of the signal being picked up?

_____ (b)

(a) ellipse becomes a straight line

(b) ellipse closes to a straight line and then opens again

4.83 You need to measure the phase shift of a network over a range of frequencies from 100 c/s to 100 kc/s. You know that the sign of the phase angle is positive at low frequencies, so you decide to use the Webb mask. As you vary the frequency from 100 c/s to 100 kc/s, the phase angle varies continuously and you observe the following sequence:

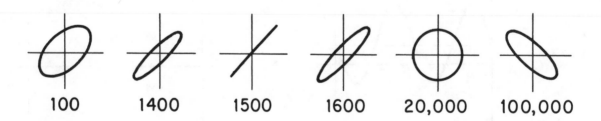

| 100 | 1400 | 1500 | 1600 | 20,000 | 100,000 |

The ellipse closes only at 1500 c/s as shown. Over what frequency range, if any, is the phase angle negative? _____

an ellipse (or a circle if the peak x and y deflections are equal)

1.93   Obtain an R-C network (R = 220,000 ohms, C = 10 microfarads) from the supervisor and connect the circuit as shown in frame 1.92 using the low frequency function generator as a sine-wave source. With the frequency set to 1 c/s, make the necessary adjustments* so that the spot travels in an approximately circular path. (Adjustment of the vertical gain, both calibrated and uncalibrated as well as the position may be necessary.)

If you have trouble getting your circuit to function properly, turn to frame 1.94.

Which direction does the spot travel around the circle?

_____ clockwise _____

Turn to frame 1.95.

*[503 ONLY--Set the horizontal sensitivity to 2 volts/cm.]

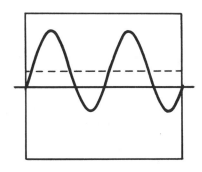

Note that the sweep now triggers when the entire waveform goes through zero instead of when the AC component is zero.

If you had difficulty with frames 2.87 and 2.88, review frames 2.39-2.44 before continuing.

2.90   Disconnect the DC source and set up the scope to display 2 cycles of a 500 c/s triangular wave with an amplitude of 4 squares peak-to-peak. Set slope to +, trigger level to 0, and trigger coupling to AC. Observe the effect of moving the wave up and down with the position control.

Does the waveform shift sideways? _____ (a)

Now switch to DC trigger coupling and observe the effect of using the vertical position control. Does the waveform shift sideways? _____ (b)

Explain why the waveform shifts sideways in one case and not in the other. _____

_____

_____ (c)

(If you can't explain it, review frame 2.45.)

3.94 An adaptor plug is available which converts the three-terminal grounding plug on the scope line cord to a two-terminal plug without ground. Attach such an adaptor plug to the line plug on the scope. When the adaptor plug is in place, the ground terminals on the scope panel (are/are not) _____ connected to the building   (a) ground.

With the adaptor plug in place, is the 60 c/s pickup more or less than when the scope is grounded to the building ground? _____   (b)

Leave the adaptor plug connected for the rest of Lab Part III. This will make it easier to observe the effects of hum and noise pickup.

f > 1500 c/s

4.84 The phase shift of a network is to be measured over a wide range of frequencies. Each time the frequency is changed the time axis must be recalibrated if you are using the _____ method.   (a)

However, it is unnecessary to calibrate either axis precisely when using the _____ method.   (b)

If you wish to make a series of phase measurements over a wide range of frequencies without having to change the circuit connections, you should use the _____ method.   (c)

If the sign of the phase angle is not known and you wish to determine it, you should use the _____ method.   (d)

1.94 (a) Check your circuit to make sure that it is connected as shown in diagram below. Pay particular attention to the grounds.

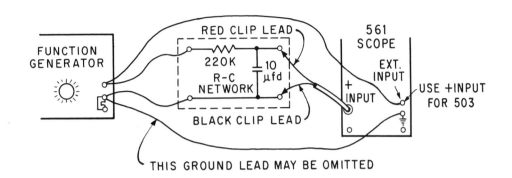

(b) Adjust function generator output amplitude to give desired trace width on screen.

(c) If the trace moves off the screen when you adjust the VOLTS/DIV switch and it cannot be brought back with the position control, ask your supervisor to check the DC balance on your scope and to check the oscillator for a DC output.

Now turn back to frame 1.93.

(a) No   (b) Yes

(c) for AC coupling the DC level introduced by the position control is removed and has no effect

---

2.91 (a) Set the scope to display exactly 4 cycles of a 500 c/s triangular wave.

(b) Now switch the trigger source to LINE. Can a stable picture be obtained? _____

(c) Explain. _____

(d) Suppose that the INT position of the SOURCE switch was defective and could not be used. With the vertical input the same as in (a), how would you set up the scope so that a stable picture could be obtained?

_____

_____

(e) Verify your answer to (d) experimentally.

(a) are not   (b) more (If you observed less or no change, your scope
                         might have a bad plug on the line cord; ask the
                         supervisor to check.)

3.95 | Electric and magnetic fields of line frequency are always present in the lab (or anywhere in the vicinity of AC power lines, motors, transformers, and AC operated equipment). These stray fields will induce unwanted signals in our leads if we do not take the proper precautions. The magnitude of the signal picked up by a circuit will depend on its impedance.

Connect a second long lead to the ground terminal below the +INPUT. Stretch out the leads to nearly full length and connect them to a one megohm resistor mounted on the circuit board. Observe the amplitude of the 60 c/s hum signal which is displayed on the screen. Repeat with the resistance changed to 100 kilohms, 10 kilohms, and 1 kilohm:

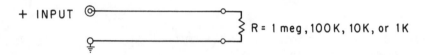

The amplitude of the hum signal which is picked up is largest for
_____ (high/low) impedance circuits.

(a) trig. sweep   (b) ellipse   (c) ellipse   (d) trig. sweep

---

4.85 | When making phase measurements by the ellipse method it may be necessary to change plug-ins if (a) the horizontal signal is too small to drive the horizontal amplifier in the time base or (b) the frequency of the signal is too high. Change the plug-ins* so that you have a 3A75 amplifier in both channels. (A 2A63 or 63 may be used in both channels if two 3A75's are not available.) If the amplifiers are identical, the phase shift error should be zero at all frequencies. Check the phase shift error over the frequency range 20 c/s to 40 kc. What is the maximum phase shift error in this range? _____

561
ONLY

*See frame 3.76 if you have forgotton how to change plug-ins.

can't do mathematically

counterclockwise (compare this with the answer obtained in the preparation, frame 1.31) ?

1.95 As derived in the preparation, with $v_h = V_h \sin \omega t$, $v_v \approx V_h/\omega RC \cos \omega t$. Explain why the vertical sensitivity must be changed in order to maintain circular trace as the frequency is increased. _____ *impedance changes increasingly; i. Vv decreases, so Sv must be increased*

Now gradually increase the frequency from 1 c/s to 10 c/s and observe the effect on the trace. As you increase the frequency, make the necessary adjustments to maintain an approximately circular trace.

(If the trace moves off the screen when you adjust the VOLTS/DIV switch and it cannot be brought back with the position control, ask the lab supervisor to check the DC balance on your scope and to check the function generator for a DC output.)

(a) Note that the sweep must be uncalibrated to obtain the required trace.

(b) No.

(c) 500 c/s is not a multiple of 60 c/s, so the sweep will trigger at a different point in each cycle (i.e., the vertical input and sweep are not synchronized).

(d) Set the SOURCE to EXT and connect the EXT TRIGGER input in parallel with the vertical input.

(e) If you didn't get a stable picture, try again.

2.92 This completes Part II. You should now understand how to use the triggering controls to display periodic waveforms on the scope.

3.96 Reconnect the 1 megohm resistor to the long leads.

Connect a second 1 megohm resistor to the -INPUT and ground with short leads (about 6 or 8 inches). Switch back and forth between the +INPUT and -INPUT using the AC-DC-GND switches and compare the relative amplitudes of the signals.

Hum pickup can be reduced by using _____ _____.

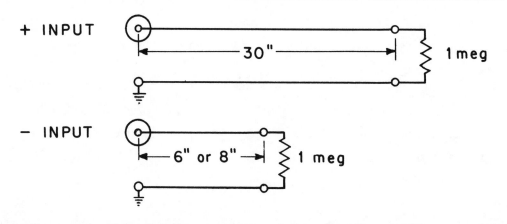

To check the phase shift error, connect the oscillator output to both plug-ins (+INPUT on 2A63's). Maximum error should be 1° or less. (If your answer is greater than 1°, ask the supervisor to check.)

4.86 [561: Be sure to use two identical plug-ins for (a), (b) and (c) of this frame.] This frame will test your ability to make phase measurements by the ellipse and triggered sweep methods.

Remove the Webb mask.

Connect the network as follows and measure the phase shift by the ellipse method at f = 5000 c/s. (Note that there is a common ground between v_1 and v_2; therefore, use of the -INPUT is unnecessary.)

$|\theta|$ = _____ = _____. (a)

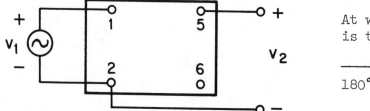

At what frequency (if any) is the phase shift 0°?

_____ (b)

180°? _____ (c)

Check your answer to (a) by the triggered sweep method.

θ = _____ (d)

v_v decreases as frequency is increased (so S_v must be changed to compensate)

1.96 For each of the following scope traces, the vertical input is
v_v = 2 cos ωt.
The horizontal sensitivity is 1 volt/div.
In each case determine the horizontal input voltage and vertical sensitivity.

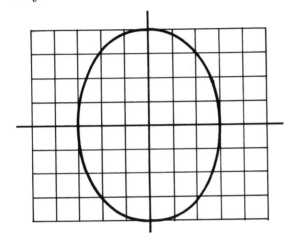 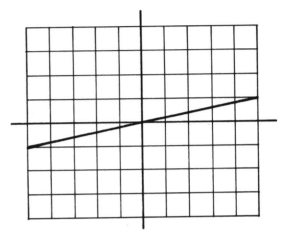

(a) $v_h(t)$ = _____ 3 sin ωt _____   (c) $v_h(t)$ = _____ 5 cos ωt _____

(b) S_v = _____ .5 v/div _____   (d) S_v = _____ 2 v/div _____

Check your answers by considering limiting values before you turn the page.
(Note that answers to (a) and (c) should be time functions.)

3.97 Disconnect the short leads from the -INPUT. Connect a long lead to the ungrounded output terminal of the sine-wave oscillator and stretch it out across the leads connected to the +INPUT of the scope (see diagram below). Set the oscillator to 10 kc/s, turn the oscillator amplitude all the way up, and observe the signal which is picked up by the scope leads. The observed signal will consist of a 10 kc signal with some 60-cycle added to it. It should look like this:

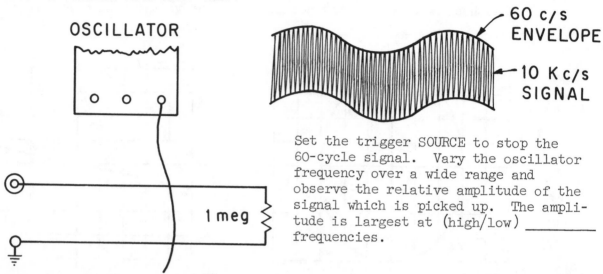

OSCILLATOR

1 meg

60 c/s ENVELOPE

10 Kc/s SIGNAL

Set the trigger SOURCE to stop the 60-cycle signal. Vary the oscillator frequency over a wide range and observe the relative amplitude of the signal which is picked up. The amplitude is largest at (high/low) _____ frequencies.

(a,d) Answers should check within 3° (or 4°).

Before disconnecting your circuit, have your lab instructor or supervisor check your answers and sign here: _____

4.87 When we must display one voltage vs another voltage on the screen, we can either use the EXT. INPUT on the time base plug-in (which has a fixed gain), or we can replace the time base with an amplifier plug-in. In which of the following situations should we replace the time base plug-in with an amplifier? _____ (give letters)

561 ONLY

(a) The horizontal input voltage is very low.

(b) The horizontal input voltage is very high and cannot be reduced.

(c) Neither side of the horizontal input voltage can be grounded.

(d) The horizontal input voltage is low frequency and the amplitude is adjustable.

(e) We need to calibrate the scale of the horizontal voltage.

(f) We are trying to measure phase shift at high frequencies and do not want to compensate for phase shift error.

(a) $v_h = 3 \sin \omega t$ (c) $v_h = 5 \cos \omega t$

(b) $S_v = .5$ volts/div   (d) $S_v = 2$ volts/div

1.97 You have completed Part I. You should now understand the relation between the voltages applied to the vertical and horizontal inputs of the scope and the resulting traces on the screen. Do Preparation Part II before continuing with the lab work.

3.98 | Reset the oscillator frequency to 10 kc/s. Connect a pair of long leads to the -INPUT and ground terminals. Twist this pair of leads together and connect them to a one megohm resistor. Mount this resistor on the circuit board next to the other one (see diagram).

OSCILLATOR

1 meg

1 meg

Compare the relative amplitudes of the signals picked up by switching back and forth between the +INPUT and the -INPUT. This illustrates that pickup can be reduced by using _____

_____. (a)

Replace the untwisted leads with a shielded (coaxial cable) lead connected from the +INPUT to the resistor. Is the pickup less with the shielded lead or the twisted leads? _____ (b)

(a) (because the EXT. INPUT is too low)
(b) (because otherwise the trace would go off the screen)
(c) (because a differential amplifier would be needed)
(e) (because the EXT. INPUT gain is not calibrated)
(f) (matched plug-ins are needed because EXT. INPUT would cause phase shift error)

4.88 | Given a choice between the ellipse method and the triggered sweep method, which one would you use

(a) to find the frequency at which the phase angle is 0° or 180°? _____

(b) if you want to get a rough idea of how the phase angle varies when the frequency is varied over a wide range? _____

(c) if you must find the sign of the phase angle? _____

(d) to find the frequency at which the magnitude of the phase angle is 90°? _____

561 ONLY (e) if the frequency is high and you don't want to change plug-ins or compensate for phase shift error? _____

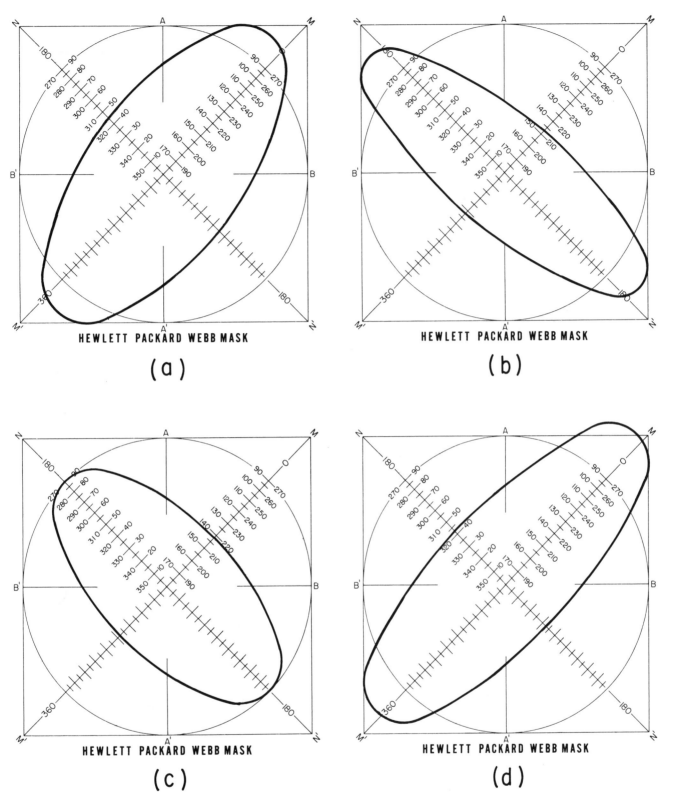

FIG. 4-50
Reproduced from HEWLETT-PACKARD Application Note No. 29 and
used by permission of HEWLETT-PACKARD COMPANY.

(a) twisted leads   (b) shielded lead

3.99 State the effect of each of the following on pickup of stray signals:

circuit impedance

_____ (a)

signal frequency

_____ (b)

lead length

_____ (c)

type of leads

_____

_____ (d)

(a) ellipse   (b) ellipse   (c) trig. sweep   (d) ellipse
(When searching for a given phase angle like 0°, 90° or 180°, the ellipse
method is easier because the triggered sweep method requires changing
connections to recalibrate the time axis each time the frequency is changed.)
(e) trig. sweep

4.89 You have now completed Lab Part IV. You should know how to measure phase
shift accurately by the triggered sweep method, the ellipse method, and
by using the Webb mask.

Part **V** consists of a review and summary of the material covered in the
first four parts. You may wish to study Part V as a review before you
take the practical laboratory examination on use of the oscilloscope.

TABLE 4-1

Phase shift for lattice network number _____

Measured using oscillator number _____

FREQUENCY (c/s)	θ MEASURED BY TRIGGERED SWEEP	θ MEASURED BY ELLIPSE METHOD	θ READ FROM WEBB MASK
100			
300			
	///////////	-90	///////////
1000			
	///////////	± 180	///////////
3000			
	///////////	+90	///////////
10000			

(a) the lower the impedance, the less the pickup

(b) the higher the frequency, the more the pickup

(c) the shorter the leads, the less the pickup

(d) straight leads pick up most, twisted leads somewhat less, and shielded leads the least.

3.100   Remove the adaptor plug from the line cord.

Look at your answer to frame 3.92. If your answer is more than 20 minutes you need more practice, so go back and rework frame 3.92.

This completes Lab Part III. You should be able to check the scope calibration and adjust the probe so that the scope can be used to make accurate measurements of voltage or time. You should now understand the functions of all of the scope controls except the sweep stability. (Adjustment of the sweep stability is discussed in Section 5.7.)

PART V   REVIEW AND SUMMARY

This part consists mainly of a summary of the material presented in the first four parts arranged for more convenient reference. The appropriate parts of the programmed instruction in Parts I through IV should be studied before reading this review.

5.1 Functions of the Scope Controls and Inputs

The functions of the scope controls and inputs are summarized below. Numbers and letters refer to Fig. 5-1 for the Tektronix 561 (or 561A,B) scope and to Fig. 5-2 for the Tektronix 503 scope.

1. INTENSITY controls brightness of the trace. Excessive intensity can burn the screen, especially if the spot is stationary. To avoid possible damage to the screen, turn down the intensity before turning the scope on.

2. FOCUS controls sharpness of the trace. Adjust for a fine, sharp trace.

2A. ASTIGMATISM is used in conjunction with the focus control. Occasional adjustment may be necessary to obtain a round spot or to obtain a uniform focus over the entire screen.

3. VERTICAL POSITION moves the trace up and down.

4. HORIZONTAL POSITION moves the trace sideways.

5. VERTICAL SENSITIVITY (VOLTS/DIV) determines the vertical input voltage required to deflect the spot one division.

6. VARIABLE VOLTS/DIV allows a smooth (rather than step-wise) variation of the vertical sensitivity. The marked values of VOLTS/DIV apply only when the red VARIABLE knob is in the calibrated position (rotated fully counterclockwise past the click stop).

5A. (503 ONLY) HORIZONTAL SENSITIVITY determines the horizontal input voltage required to deflect the spot one division.

6A. (503 ONLY) VARIABLE operates the same as (6) except horizontal sensitivity is varied.

7. AC-DC-GND input switch selects the coupling between the +INPUT and the vertical amplifier. The AC position inserts a blocking capacitor so that only the AC component of the input is displayed. The DC position is direct coupled so that the entire input is displayed. DC should be used for low frequencies. The GND position grounds the amplifier input so the deflection is zero.

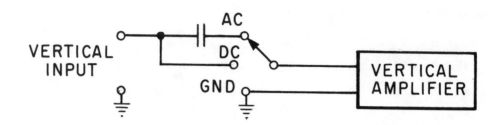

8. Same as (7) except -INPUT is affected.

7A. and 8A. (503 ONLY) Same as (7) and (8) for horizontal amplifier.

9. AC STABILIZED (561 ONLY) may be turned ON to prevent the trace from drifting when measuring small AC signals in the 1 millivolt to 20 millivolt range. It must be turned OFF when measuring DC or low frequency signals. A warning light turns on if AC STABILIZED is ON when the input switch is set to DC.

10. DC BALANCE adjusts the output of the vertical amplifier so that it is zero when the inputs are grounded. If DC BALANCE is out of adjustment the trace will move off the screen when VOLTS/DIV is rotated toward the 1 mv range.

10A. (503 ONLY) Same as (10) for horizontal amplifier.

11. GAIN ADJ. (561 ONLY) adjusts the vertical amplifier gain. The VOLTS/DIV values on the panel are correct only when the gain is properly adjusted. Readjustment of the gain is necessary whenever a plug-in is changed from one scope to another.

12. CALIBRATION (561 ONLY) is used to calibrate the sweep time. The TIME/DIV values on the panel are correct only when the sweep time is properly calibrated.

13. CALIBRATOR SWITCH (561 ONLY) selects the peak-to-peak voltage which appears at the CAL. OUT connector (E). This voltage is a square wave which can be used when adjusting the vertical gain, calibrating the sweep time, or adjusting the probe compensation. Square wave frequency is 60 c/s for 561 and 561A, 1000 c/s for 561B.

14. SWEEP TIME/CM (TIME/DIV) selects the time required for the spot to travel one division across the screen.

15. VARIABLE TIME/DIV allows a smooth variation of the sweep rate. The marked values of TIME/DIV apply only when the red VARIABLE knob is in the calibrated position. [561 ONLY: There is no click stop on the VARIABLE TIME/DIV knob; a light comes on when it is not in the CALIBRATED position. Pull out the VARIABLE knob to turn on the SWEEP MAGNIFIER, which expands the trace horizontally by a factor of 5.] [503 ONLY: The VARIABLE knob is in the CALIBRATED position when it is rotated full counterclockwise past the click stop.]

16. TRIGGERING LEVEL controls the voltage level of the triggering signal at which the sweep triggers. When set to AUTO the sweep automatically triggers when no triggering signal is present, and it triggers at a level near zero when a triggering signal is present. When set to FREE RUN a repetitive sweep is obtained which is not synchronized with any triggering signal which may be present.

17. TRIGGERING SLOPE causes triggering to occur either on the positive (+) slope of triggering signal or on the negative (-) slope. (The SLOPE cannot be set to trigger on a zero slope.)

18. TRIGGER COUPLING selects the coupling between the triggering signal and the sweep circuits. The AC position inserts a blocking capacitor so that only the AC component of the triggering signal affects the sweep. The DC position is direct coupled so that the entire triggering signal (including the DC component) controls the level at which the sweep triggers. DC coupling should be used for low frequencies. [561 ONLY: AC SLOW coupling is used for most purposes. AC FAST has a smaller blocking capacitor and is used when we want only the high frequency component of the triggering signal to trigger the sweep.] Setting LEVEL to AUTO automatically selects AC (AC SLOW) coupling.

19. TRIGGER SOURCE selects the source of the triggering signal. When set to INTernal the source is the output of the vertical amplifier so that in effect the vertical input signal controls the triggering. When set to LINE the sweep is triggered by the 60 c/s AC line. When set to EXTernal, an external triggering signal must be connected to the EXT. TRIG. input (H).

20. HORIZONTAL DISPLAY (503 ONLY) connects the horizontal amplifier input to either the sweep generator or to an external signal which is connected to the +INPUT (I) or -INPUT (J). The trace can be expanded horizontally 2, 5, 10, 20 or 50 times when the appropriate SWEEP MAGNIFIED position is used.

21. SWEEP STABILITY adjustment is explained in Section 5.7.

22. MODE (561 with 2B67 Time Base only) allows selection of NORMal
    (repetitive sweep) or SINGLE SWEEP operation. When the MODE lever
    is moved to RESET and released to the SINGLE SWEEP position, the
    sweep is ready to be triggered as indicated by the READY light.
    After the sweep has been triggered once, it must be reset before it
    can be retriggered. Returning the MODE switch to NORM permits re-
    petitive triggering of the sweep.

Terminals B, D and G as well as the outer conductors on connectors A and C are
all grounds. This means they are all connected to the scope case and chassis,
which is in turn connected to the building ground through the third wire in the
line cord.

Terminal F (561 only) is the EXTernal INPUT to the horizontal amplifier. When
an external horizontal input is used, set TIME/DIV to EXT. INPUT in order to
disable the sweep. The horizontal sensitivity is not adjustable on the 2B67 (67)
TIME BASE plug-in; it is fixed at roughly 1 volt/div. If different horizontal
sensitivities are needed, exchange the TIME BASE plug-in for an amplifier plug-in.

Terminals K and L (503 only) provide 500 mv and 5 mv peak-to-peak square waves
which can be used to check the calibration of the vertical and horizontal amplifiers and for adjusting the probe compensation.

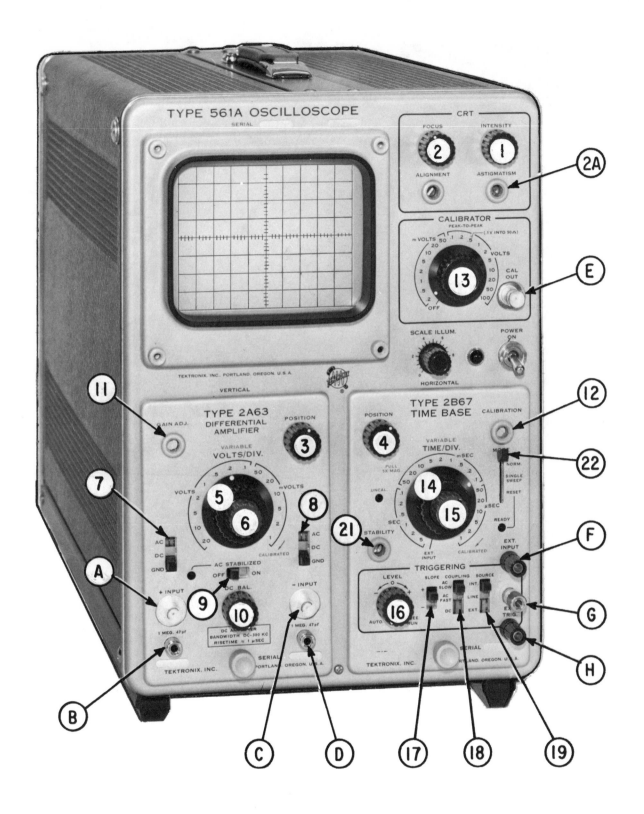

FIG. 5-1. TEKTRONIX 561A OSCILLOSCOPE
(with 2A63 DIFFERENTIAL AMPLIFIER and 2B67 TIME BASE)

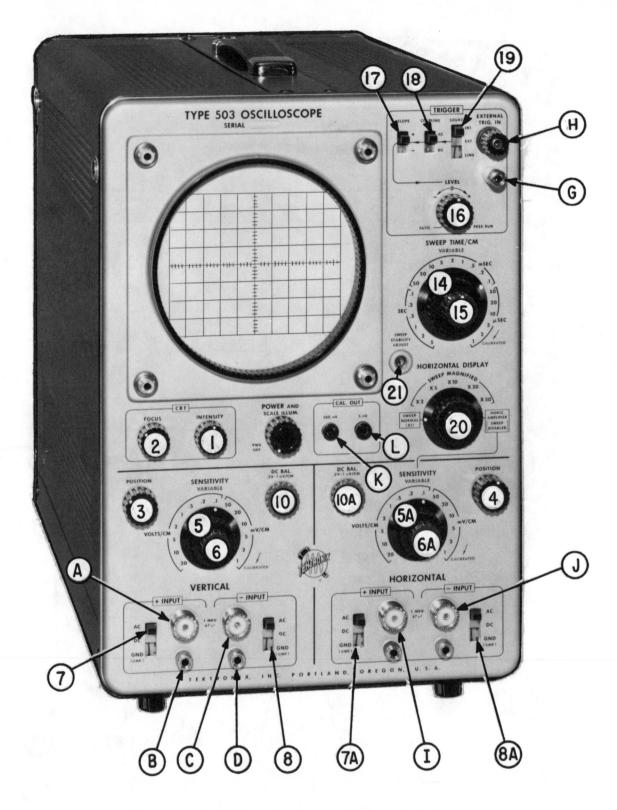

FIG. 5-2. TEKTRONIX 503 OSCILLOSCOPE

5.2   X-Y Operation of the Scope

The oscilloscope can be operated in two basic modes--the X-Y mode in which the input signals to <u>both</u> the horizontal and vertical amplifiers come from external sources, and the sweep mode in which the horizontal amplifier input is a sweep waveform generated within the scope.   The X-Y mode is used to display one voltage against another, while the sweep mode is used to display a voltage as a function of time.   In the X-Y mode, a positive voltage applied between the horizontal scope input and ground causes the spot on the screen to deflect to the right and a negative voltage to the left.   The horizontal deflection in divisions is $x = v_h/S_h$ where v_h is the horizontal input voltage and S_h is the horizontal sensitivity in volts/div.   A positive voltage applied between the vertical input and ground causes upward deflection of the spot and a negative voltage downward deflection.   The vertical deflection in divisions is $y = v_v/S_v$ where v_v is the vertical input voltage and S_v is the vertical sensitivity.

If the signals applied to the vertical and horizontal inputs change slowly, the spot will move slowly on the screen.   If the signals are periodic and the frequency is high enough, the spot will retrace the same path fast enough that a solid trace will appear on the screen, and no flicker will be observed because of persistence of the screen.   If v_v and v_h are related by a constant, i.e., $v_v(t) = K\, v_h(t)$, the trace will be a diagonal line; if v_v and v_h are sine waves which are not in phase, the trace will be circular or elliptical.

5.3   Displaying Waveforms as a Function of Time

In order to display a waveform as a function of time, the horizontal deflection must be proportional to time $(x = Kt)$.   The necessary horizontal signal is provided by the TIME BASE (see Fig. 5-3).   Each time the TIME BASE is triggered, it produces a sweep waveform of the following form:

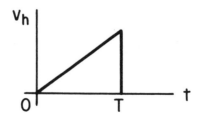

This waveform causes the spot to sweep across the screen once in T seconds and then return to the left edge of the screen. The rate at which the spot sweeps across the screen is determined by the TIME/DIV switch. If the sweep rate is R sec/div, the time required for the spot to travel X div is t = R X.

In order to display a steady picture on the screen, the sweep waveform must be repeated periodically, and it must be synchronized with the waveform being observed. This synchronization is accomplished by means of a triggering signal. This triggering signal may come from the vertical amplifier output (INTernal trigger), from the 60 c/s AC line (LINE trigger), or from the external trigger input (EXTernal trigger). Internal trigger is used when we want the triggering signal to be the same as the vertical input, and external trigger is used when we want to observe the time relationship between two different wave-forms. The triggering signal may be coupled to the time base directly (DC coupling) or through a blocking capacitor (AC coupling). DC coupling is used when we want the entire signal (both AC and DC components) to affect the triggering circuit, while AC coupling is used when we want to control triggering with the AC component of the triggering signal.

The TIME BASE is composed of a trigger pulse generator and a sweep generator (Fig. 5-4). A trigger pulse is produced when the slope and level of the triggering signal match the settings of the trigger SLOPE and LEVEL controls. Each trigger pulse will trigger the sweep generator and cause the beam to sweep across the screen once, provided that the previous sweep has gone to completion. Fig. 5-5 shows an example of trigger circuit operation.

When the exact level at which triggering occurs is not important, the trigger LEVEL control may be set to AUTO. When set to AUTO, normal amplitude internal or external triggering signals will trigger the sweep at a level near zero. However, even when no internal or external trigger signal is present, the sweep is automatically triggered by a signal from within the scope so that a base line will appear on the screen. When LEVEL is set to AUTO, AC trigger coupling is selected regardless of the position of the trigger COUPLING switch. Setting LEVEL to FREE RUN produces a free-running sweep which is independent of any trigger signal.

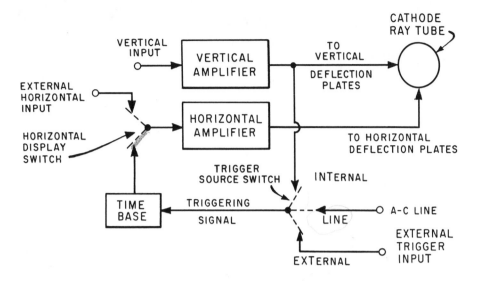

FIG. 5-3. SIMPLIFIED BLOCK DIGRAM OF OSCILLOSCOPE

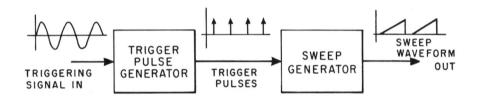

FIG. 5-4. OPERATION OF THE TIME BASE

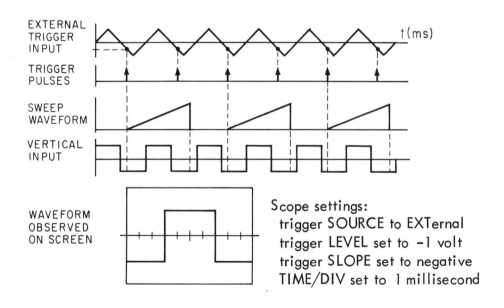

Scope settings:
trigger SOURCE to EXTernal
trigger LEVEL set to −1 volt
trigger SLOPE set to negative
TIME/DIV set to 1 millisecond

FIG. 5-5. EXAMPLE OF TRIGGER CIRCUIT OPERATION

5.4 Observing Signals with AC and DC Components

A periodic signal can have both an AC component and a DC component. Given a periodic waveform, $v(t)$, the average value is referred to as the DC component, V_{DC}. If we subtract out the DC component, the remainder is referred to as the time-varying or AC component, $v_{AC}(t)$; i.e.,

$$v_{AC}(t) = v(t) - V_{DC}$$

For the following waveform, the dashed line indicates the average or DC value and the AC component is plotted separately. Note that the average value of the AC component is zero with equal area above and below the line.

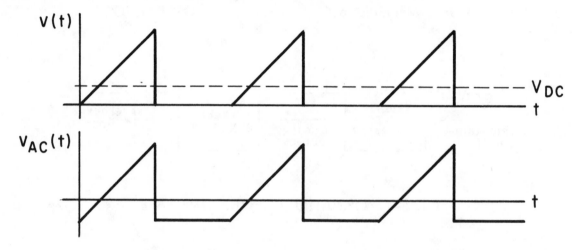

FIG. 5-6. WAVEFORM WITH AC AND DC COMPONENTS

When the input switch on the vertical amplifier is set to AC, a blocking capacitor in series with the input removes the DC component so that only the AC component is observed. When the input switch is set to DC the amplifier is direct coupled so that both the AC and DC components can be observed. The DC component of a waveform can be measured by switching the input from AC to DC and observing the vertical shift of the waveform. The DC input must be used for very low frequency signals since the impedance of the blocking capacitor $(1/\omega C)$ is not negligible at low frequencies.

5.5   The Differential Amplifier

The differential amplifier amplifies the difference of the voltages applied to the +INPUT and -INPUT terminals. If v_+ is the voltage between the +INPUT and ground and v_- is the voltage between the -INPUT and ground, the difference component of the voltages is

$$\Delta v = v_+ - v_-$$

and the common-mode component is

$$v_c = \frac{1}{2} \left(v_+ + v_- \right)$$

An ideal differential amplifier amplifies the difference component and rejects the common-mode component, so the vertical deflection is

$$y = \frac{1}{S_v} \left(v_+ - v_- \right) = K_d \, \Delta v$$

where $K_d = 1/S_v$ is the difference mode gain. If the amplifier is not perfect all of the common-mode component will not be rejected so

$$y = K_d \, \Delta v + K_c \, v_c = K_d \left(v_+ - v_- \right) + K_c \, \frac{v_+ + v_-}{2}$$

where K_c is the common-mode gain. The common-mode gain can be measured by applying a sine wave to both the +INPUT and -INPUT. With $v_+ = v_- = V_p \sin \omega t$ the observed deflection is

$$y = K_c \, V_p \sin \omega t = y_1 \sin \omega t$$

so $K_c = y_1/V_p$ div/volt. The common-mode rejection ratio is defined as

$$CMRR = K_d/K_c$$

An ideal differential amplifier has an infinite CMRR, and a good differential amplifier will have a CMRR greater than 100.

The error in the observed deflection may be significant if the common-mode signal is too large or if CMRR is too low. This error will be negligible if

$$\left| K_c v_c \right| \ll \left| K_d \Delta v \right| \qquad \text{or} \qquad CMRR = \frac{K_d}{K_c} \gg \left| \frac{v_c}{\Delta v} \right|$$

Table 5-1 shows the maximum voltage which can be applied to the differential amplifier inputs. If this maximum is exceeded, the waveform may be distorted even though the difference of the v+ and v- inputs is small.

TABLE 5-1   Maximum Input Voltage to Differential Amplifier

VOLTS/DIV setting	Maximum voltage to either input (561)	Maximum voltage to either input (503)
1 mv to .2 volts	± 5 volts	± 2 volts
.5, 1, or 2 volts	± 50 volts	± 20 volts
5, 10, or 20 volts	± 500 volts	± 200 volts

The differential amplifier is useful when neither terminal of the signal being observed can be grounded. It is also useful when measuring low-level signals in the presence of noise. For example, if

$$v_+ = v_{signal} + v_{noise} \quad \text{and} \quad v_- = v_{noise}$$

the vertical deflection will be

$$y = K_d \left(\Delta v + \frac{K_c}{K_d} v_c \right) = K_d \left(v_{signal} + \frac{v_{noise}}{CMRR} \right)$$

so that most of the noise is rejected if CMRR is large.

5.6 Making Connections to the Scope

All of the "ground" terminals on the scope are connected together through the scope case and chassis, and they are connected to the building ground through the 3-wire line cord. Be careful not to short out part of your circuit by connecting two different points in the circuit to ground.

When observing low amplitude signals, precautions are necessary to prevent excessive pickup of hum and noise. Keep your leads short and use a shielded cable if necessary.

The following rules should normally be used when making connections to a scope with a differential amplifier input:

(a) If some point in the circuit is grounded, connect the circuit ground to the scope ground. (Do not rely on the line cord grounds for a connection.)

(b) If a voltage to be connected to the scope has one side grounded, then use the +INPUT on the differential amplifier. (Ground the -INPUT with a switch.)

(c) If a voltage to be connected to the scope has neither side in common with the circuit ground, use both the +INPUT and -INPUT on the differential amplifier.

214

5.7 Adjusting and Calibrating the Scope

DC BALANCE. The DC BALANCE control must be adjusted so that the output of the differential amplifier is zero when the inputs are zero; otherwise, the trace will go off the screen when the sensitivity control is rotated toward the most sensitive ranges. After the scope is thoroughly warmed up, proceed as follows to adjust the vertical DC balance:

(a) Obtain a horizontal line on the screen with both input switches set to GND and sensitivity to 0.2 volts/div.(calibrated). Center the line with the position control.

(b) Rotate the sensitivity switch toward 1 mV/div. Use the DC BALANCE if required to keep the trace on the screen. With the switch set to 1 mV/div, center the trace with the DC BALANCE.

(c) Check to see that the trace does not move when the VOLTS/DIV switch is rotated from one end to the other. If it does move, repeat (a) and (b).

Calibration of the Vertical Amplifier Gain. The scope has a built-in square wave voltage source which you can use to check the calibration. Connect the calibrator output to the vertical input (input switch set to DC to avoid distortion) and observe several cycles of the square wave. Choose a volts/div setting which should give a peak-to-peak deflection of 5 divisions [4 div for 561B]. 561: Adjust the screwdriver GAIN ADJ. to give exactly 5 divisions [4 div.] peak-to-peak deflection. 503: If the observed deflection has an error of more than 3% (0.15 div), the scope should be recalibrated by the technician.

Calibration of the Time Base (561 only). Observe the 60 c/s [1000 c/s for 561B] calibrator output waveform with the TIME/DIV switch set to 5 msec/div [0.2 msec/div]. Adjust the screwdriver CALIBRATION adjustment on the time base to give exactly 3 cycles [2 cycles] on the screen.

Sweep Stability. The time base has a screwdriver STABILITY adjustment which affects the operation of the triggering circuits. Adjustment of this control is rarely necessary, but instructions are included here for completeness. Two conditions under which sweep stability adjustment may be required are:

(a) A trace is present when trigger LEVEL is set to FREE RUN but not when it is set to AUTO.

(b) The scope has good input signal of sufficient amplitude, but the trace is jittery and cannot be synchronized for any settings of the triggering controls.

The following procedure can be used to adjust the sweep stability:

(a) With TIME/DIV set to .1 msec/div and trigger LEVEL set to FREE RUN, obtain a horizontal line on the screen.

(b) Set trigger LEVEL to AUTO and rotate the STABILITY control fully counter-clockwise so that the trace disappears.

(c) Rotate the STABILITY control slowly clockwise until a trace appears; note the position of the control.

(d) Rotate the control further clockwise until the trace brightens.

(e) Set the control about midway between the position where the trace first appears and the position where it brightens.

5.8 Loading and Use of the Probe

The equivalent circuit of the scope input is a 1 megohm resistor in parallel with a 47 pf capacitor. When the scope input is connected to a high impedance circuit, the scope loads down the circuit so that the voltage being measured is reduced. The loading effect is worse at high frequencies because of the shunt capacitance in the scope input. The loading effect can be reduced by using a probe to increase the effective input impedance of the scope. A 10X attenuating probe (such as the Tektronix P6006) attenuates (reduces) the input signal by a factor of 10, so when the probe is used the sensitivity switch setting must be multiplied by 10 to get the actual volts/div. The equivalent circuit for the probe and scope input is shown below.

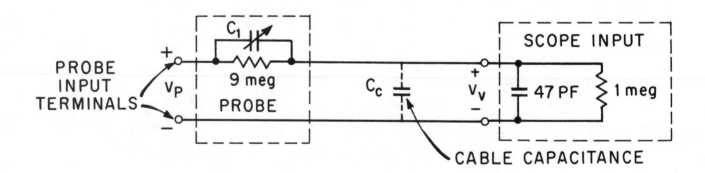

FIG. 5-7. PROBE AND SCOPE INPUT

The capacitor in the probe must be properly adjusted so that the probe attenuation is independent of frequency. This can be accomplished by using the probe to observe a square wave, and adjusting the probe so that the corners of the square wave appear square with no overshoot or rounding (see Fig. 5-8).

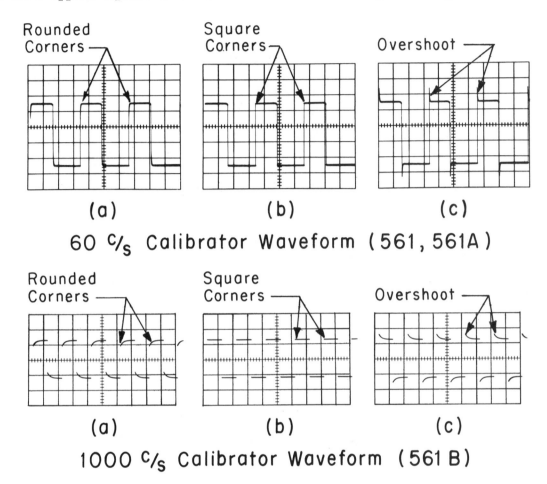

FIG. 5-8. PROBE COMPENSATION

5.9 Making Accurate Measurements with the Scope

The following steps should be taken when voltage or time must be measured accurately with the scope:

(a) Use a fine, sharply focused trace. Avoid excessive intensity.

(b) Make sure the scope is properly calibrated.

(c) Expand the portion of the trace to be measured to fill as large a part of the screen as possible.

(d) Adjust the position controls to facilitate accurate reading.

(e) To avoid parallax error, view the screen from directly in front. (This is unnecessary if the scope has an internal graticule.)

(f) Use the probe if the circuit being measured has a high impedance or if the signals are high frequency.

(g) Make sure the frequency of the signals being observed is within the bandwidth of the scope (450 kc/s for the 503 or 300 kc/s for the 561 with a 2A63 plug-in).

Even if all of the above precautions are taken in making measurements with the scope, the measured values may still have a calibration error as large as $\pm$ 3% and a reading error of $\pm$ 1/20 div or more.

5.10 Measurement of Phase Angle

Given two sinusoidal voltage $v_1(t) = A \sin \omega t$ and $v_2(t) = B \sin (\omega t + \theta)$, the phase angle θ can be determined by either the triggered sweep method or by the ellipse method. The former determines both sign and magnitude of θ and the latter determines only the magnitude.

Triggered Sweep Method. First connect v_1 to the vertical input and to the EXT. TRIG. input. With the trigger coupling set to external, display $v_1(t)$ and calibrate the time axis to 20°/div (or some other convenient value):

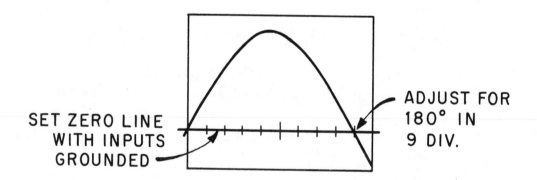

SET ZERO LINE WITH INPUTS GROUNDED

ADJUST FOR 180° IN 9 DIV.

This establishes a t = 0 reference point. Without disturbing the triggering circuit (leave v_1 connected to EXT. TRIG.), connect v_2 to the vertical input and observe v_2. If $v_2(0)$ is negative, $\theta = -\theta_1$ where θ_1 is the distance between the origin and the "0° point" on the sine wave as in Fig. 5-9. If $v_2(0)$ is positive, $\theta = 180° - \theta_2$ where θ_2 is the distance between the origin and the "180° point" on the sine wave.

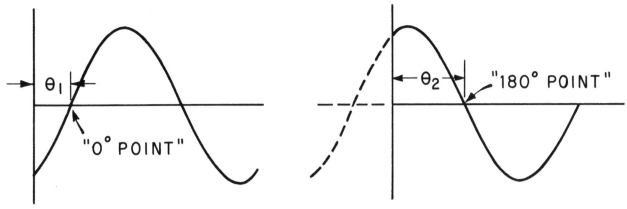

FIG. 5-9. PHASE ANGLE MEASUREMENT

Ellipse Method. Connect v_1 to the horizontal input, v_2 to the vertical input, and display v_2 vs v_1 on the screen. The magnitude of θ can be determined from Table 5-2, or it can be read directly off the trace by using a Webb mask (Fig. 4-47). The ellipse method does not give the sign of θ; however, if the sign is known at one frequency and the ellipse is observed as the frequency is varied continuously, a change of sign can be detected when the ellipse closes to a straight line and opens out again. For accurate results, the ellipse method requires that the phase shift introduced by the vertical and horizontal scope amplifiers be the same; otherwise, phase shift compensation is necessary.

Table 5-2. Determination of Phase Angle by the Ellipse Method

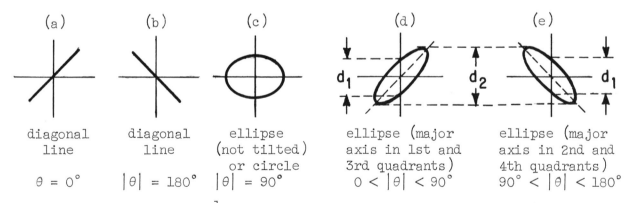

(a)	(b)	(c)	(d)	(e)
diagonal line	diagonal line	ellipse (not tilted) or circle	ellipse (major axis in 1st and 3rd quadrants)	ellipse (major axis in 2nd and 4th quadrants)
$\theta = 0°$	$|\theta| = 180°$	$|\theta| = 90°$	$0 < |\theta| < 90°$	$90° < |\theta| < 180°$

For (d) and (e), $|\theta| = \sin^{-1}(d_1/d_2)$ where d_1 is the distance between the y-axis intercepts and d_2 is the peak-to-peak vertical deflection. Ellipse must be centered horizontally.

APPENDIX

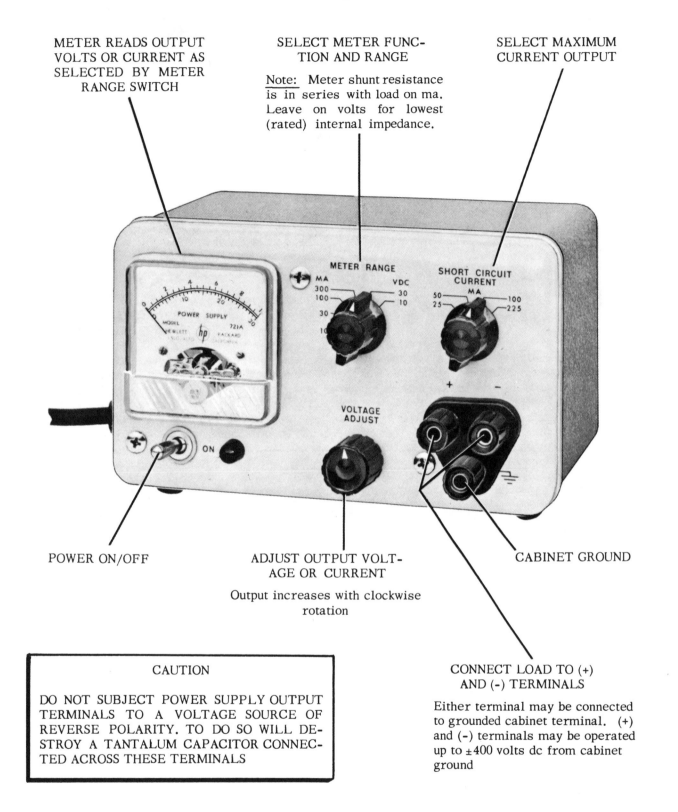

METER READS OUTPUT VOLTS OR CURRENT AS SELECTED BY METER RANGE SWITCH

SELECT METER FUNC-TION AND RANGE

Note: Meter shunt resistance is in series with load on ma. Leave on volts for lowest (rated) internal impedance.

SELECT MAXIMUM CURRENT OUTPUT

POWER ON/OFF

ADJUST OUTPUT VOLT-AGE OR CURRENT

Output increases with clockwise rotation

CABINET GROUND

CONNECT LOAD TO (+) AND (-) TERMINALS

Either terminal may be connected to grounded cabinet terminal. (+) and (-) terminals may be operated up to ±400 volts dc from cabinet ground

CAUTION

DO NOT SUBJECT POWER SUPPLY OUTPUT TERMINALS TO A VOLTAGE SOURCE OF REVERSE POLARITY. TO DO SO WILL DE-STROY A TANTALUM CAPACITOR CONNEC-TED ACROSS THESE TERMINALS

FIG. A-1. HEWLETT PACKARD MODEL 721A
POWER SUPPLY OPERATING CONTROLS
Used by permission of HEWLETT-PACKARD COMPANY.

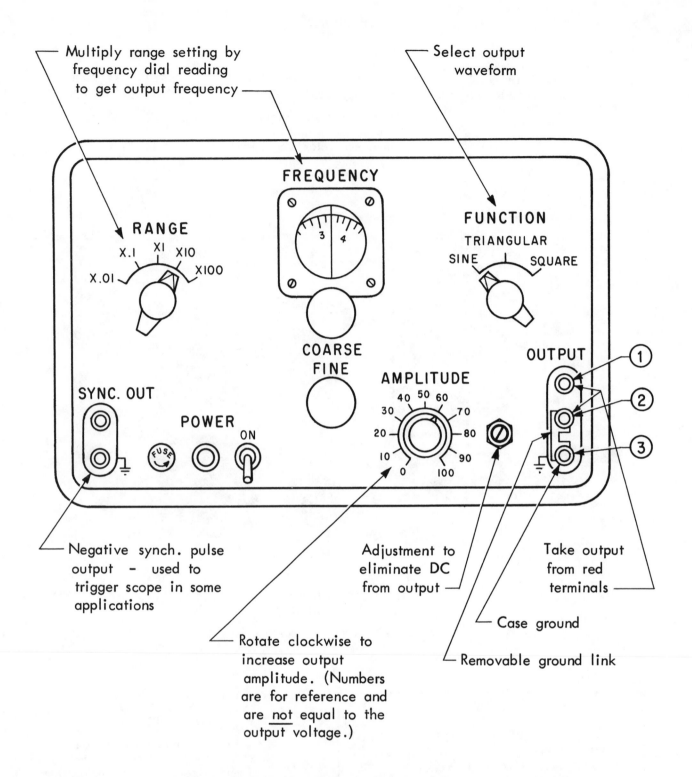

Multiply range setting by frequency dial reading to get output frequency

Select output waveform

FREQUENCY

RANGE

X.I XI XIO
X.01   X100

FUNCTION

TRIANGULAR
SINE   SQUARE

3   4

COARSE
FINE

OUTPUT

①

②

③

SYNC. OUT

POWER

ON

AMPLITUDE

40 50 60
30   70
20   80
10   90
0   100

FUSE

Negative synch. pulse output – used to trigger scope in some applications

Adjustment to eliminate DC from output

Take output from red terminals

Case ground

Removable ground link

Rotate clockwise to increase output amplitude. (Numbers are for reference and are not equal to the output voltage.)

FIG. A-2. HEWLETT-PACKARD 202A LOW FREQUENCY FUNCTION
GENERATOR
Used by permission of HEWLETT-PACKARD COMPANY.

Notes

Notes

Notes

Notes

Notes

Notes